Disillusioned Apprentice

by

David A. Ray

To Richard
Best wishes + good luck
Dave

First published in Great Britain by DAR Printing 2009

A CIP catalogue of this title is available from the British Library,

ISBN 978-0-9552926-1-3

Printed in Great Britain by the MPG Books Group, Bodmin and King's Lynn
Published by DAR Printing
8 Victoria Street,
Thurmaston,
Leicester, LE4 8GG
darprintin@btconnect.com

Thanks to

Beryl McDowall, John Booth, Marion, Evelyn,
Val Moore, Stephen Loveless, Bead Roberts,
Leicester Writing School,
Mel and Scribo,
Leicester Writers Club,
and all the others who helped.
Without their help this book wouldn't exist.
There would be no errors. All that there are, are mine
Dave Ray 2009

An old Native American Indian passing on his wisdom to his grandchildren said,
"A fight is going on inside me... It is a big fight between two wolves.
One wolf is all the bad things we hate and fear most, anger, envy, ignorance, greed,
arrogance, guilt, resentment, cowardice, lies and pride.
The other wolf is all the things we like and want most,
peace, love, learning, courage, humility, friendship, generosity, truth and compassion.
This fight goes on inside all of us."
They thought about it and then a child asked,
"Which wolf will win?" The old man replied...
"The one we feed."

Foreword

This book has been written as a memoir set in the early 1950's through to the middle 60's. The main protagonist is a young man setting out to find his place in the world. He has been brought up to respect both himself and a value structure built around the ideas of truth, freedom and justice. What he finds doesn't necessarily measure up to this ideal. Coping and coming to terms with the real world becomes the objective of his life. The events recounted are true though they happened forty years ago and have been written in such a way as to draw them together to make an enjoyable narrative. Some names and characteristics of individuals have been changed.

R. A. Butler's Education Act of 1944 made real changes to the accessibility of education to ordinary working people. Total war meant total use of resources and the greatest resource of a society is its people. The new world order that grew up with the industrial revolution - where technology and manufacturing capacity was more important than weight of numbers - caused contemporaries to look anew at the way society was organised. After failing to achieve any lasting remedy to the economic problems besetting the world in the period leading up to and after the First World War, the tremendous costs both material and emotional to all involved made it clear that a new approach was needed if any real solution was to be reached. Education would have as great a role to play as any other factor in winning wars as well as maintaining peace. It was these developments that saw the beginning of the end of the old system where class privilege was virtually unassailable.

After the Second World War the new approach to economics advocated by J M Keynes was being implemented. Many people have documented those changes in many ways. The majority probably aimed to provide a clear and truthful insight into what was going on. Most of those people came from the better off and more privileged classes, because it was only they who could afford an education at the time.

As is so often the case with histories, the prejudices of those

1

writing show through in the accounts given. This book sets out in some small way to redress the balance of assessments of the period and provide a view looking from nearer the bottom of the social scale upwards. Opinions as to what constitutes poverty vary with experience. I read a book some time ago about the social reformer Annie Besant. The author described her as poor when she went to India, where she bought a newspaper. She didn't go to a street vendor. She bought the business that published it. If that's poverty, then I'd like some.

I lived in Dagenham. In relation to others on the estate I didn't see myself as poor, nor well off, though better off than many. Education was valued by many on the estate as a means of social advancement and by some as an end in itself. Too often these days the real value of education is misunderstood. A qualification in beauty therapy or leisure pool management certainly has its value, but without any consideration of the social context in which such a qualification exists, its value is lessened and its holder becomes little more than a robot. Everything in society has its value, but if we fail to consider why, that value is reduced. In its own small way this book is a plea, like Tony Blair's, for education, education, education. It comes at a cost and can't be bought by weight. Truth, freedom and justice are similar and it seems to me there's a link. A hundred years ago a person who could read and write might have been regarded as reasonably educated. Now that's not enough. Before we try to provide an education we must first define what education is. In doing so, perhaps we will achieve the objective.

Dave Ray, Leicester, UK 2009

2

Dagenham

My Mother told me with an awkward grin "You're here because of a defective Rendel. They were suppositories supposed to kill sperm before they reached their target. Everything was in short supply at the end of the war. Chemicals were no different and it's more than likely that the Rendel Company were using sub-standard ingredients, so they didn't work as well as they should. That's how you came about."

Whether the Rendel was defective is anybody's guess. I like to think that the sperm that did the job was particularly tough and tenacious. It was February the fifth 1946 when I was born, almost exactly nine months after VE Day. My existence might have nothing to do with Rendels. I could be an outcome of the euphoria of the day. I like to think of myself as the product of a celebration. Who knows whether I'm here because of an extra whisky, a smile, a touch or hug brought on by the occasion? The celebrations were carried on with an enthusiasm Mum didn't whole-heartedly share. Our front gate was burnt on a bonfire and Mum complained long and hard through the early years of my childhood about our missing gate until the council replaced it. Maybe I'm the product of a farcical cycle of events centred round an incinerated front gate. Perhaps, in some odd way, she linked my existence to our missing front gate? I'll never know, but it's fun to guess.

The events preceding my arrival might not have been an ideal start, but I don't feel that way. My parents explained that they had decided to limit the family size, not simply because of a shortage of cash, but because there were already two girls. Another girl would have been a disappointment. When I entered the world with all the normal attributes of a boy, plus big black eyebrows causing the hospital staff to nickname me George Roby (a celebrity of the day with bushy eyebrows), I was welcomed as a rounding off of a normal healthy family. They convinced me that my conception was regarded as a stroke of good fortune. What wasn't so fortunate was that the family home was in Dagenham, on the Beacontree Estate - the biggest council estate ever built.

The houses were designed to do a job. They were basic, inspired less by architectural excellence than economy. At the peak of the building programme they were finishing ninety-eight houses a week. They were the "homes fit for heroes" promised by Lloyd George after the First World War. We weren't heroic nor were the houses; but neither were they slums, nor we slum dwellers. It took them ten years to get around to starting the project, and Mum, along with other cynics, would say they only started then because working people were sick of unemployment, and were getting "bolshie". Some might argue that the war was fought to set the world economy on the move again after the depression. My Dad used to talk about cost plus ten. That's what the government paid contractors during the war – cost including profit plus ten percent. Everybody worked flat out and money was thrown around 'like there was no tomorrow.' It didn't matter there was little to buy and little time to buy it.

Two years into the war Beveridge made his report. It was published when British prospects looked bleak. Churchill was making heroic speeches, but the truth was, we were losing. The people of Dagenham responded and took rationing in their stride. They worked through the blitz. When the war ended, it was payback time. What could be accomplished in war could be accomplished in peace. Churchill led the country through World War II with wonderful speeches and promises of a better world thereafter. People still remembered the unemployment following World War I. Bevin had sent one in every ten to mine coal, without fear or favour. It looked like democracy and the people of Dagenham wanted more. Attlee was elected with the biggest landslide in the history of Parliament. The days of 'them' were numbered. Now it would be as in war - us.

About a hundred thousand people lived in Dagenham, near

enough the same number as live in Bedford today, and half those employed worked in Ford's giant car plant. If there was a strike at the factory, the pubs started to close for two or three days a week. In the second week of a stoppage the butchers started shutting their doors. If the docks struck as well, Dagenham died.

It was a queer place. I remember it as not quite monochrome. You may have an idea of what council estates are like, but Dagenham was different because it was so big. Everyone who lived there was working class so everything for miles around was working class. It's not like that on smaller estates; there are always houses not far away where people have some spare cash, but not in Dagenham. It was greyer than most council estates too: most have grass verges somewhere, but not Dagenham. All there was where we lived were trees fifty yards apart on the bus routes where the roads were a bit wider. I never found out what sort they were. The council pruned them yearly so they never grew more than fifteen feet tall. In winter their straight trunks forked into a few short branches pruned into black arthritic knees and elbows, ending in knobbly, knuckles and fists. With spring, irrepressible nature began to reassert itself. Green shoots sprouted and leaves began to unfurl. The council in its ruthless wisdom responded with systematic lopping reminiscent of the ruthless suppression of independent activity among tenants that might be the precursor of an outpouring of emotion, or an expression of spirit that hinted at the undermining of their authority. The houses were decorated to a uniform pattern and individual deviation from council approved colour schemes was forbidden. Tenants were so grateful for simple decent accommodation that resistance wasn't even considered.

The estate was a massive improvement on the slums of East London it replaced. Autumn still brought pea-soupers when the street lights almost disappeared in sulphurous murk, everything tasted of soot, and buses were led by people on foot, but terrible overcrowding was a thing of the past. The horrors recounted by Dickens were gone. Beverage's recommendations would be implemented because the powers that be had no stomach for the kind of trouble there'd been in Russia and Eastern Europe. In Dagenham a Communist candidate had polled 5000 votes. Those at the top of the pyramid could feel the foundations turning to sand. They were worried. There was an army coming home and it wouldn't be fobbed off lightly.

∞∞∞∞

2

Dad's Tale

As children my parents slept three and four to a bed. My Dad explained to me only half joking. "Feet don't smell if you don't wear shoes. You know that when you sleep top to tail. That's how we used to do it. The older ones slept with their heads to the headboard and youngest slept heads to the footboard. The girls had one bed we had the other. Seven of us slept in one room. We had to climb over one another to get to our place. You get used to anything after a while."

When Dad explained something or told stories his thoughts had a knack of meandering away to a place where he totally lost track. He lost control and thoughts developed a will of their own. All too often they wandered so far that they got lost in the labyrinth of his mind and he forgot where he started. I have to watch it myself or I start to ramble but my Dad was worse. He could get from sleeping top to tail as kids, to describing in detail what a good dinner he had yesterday, in ten short sentences. It would have taken a mind reader to follow his train of thought, and sometimes I couldn't make sense of what he said.

I asked "Did your brothers really bite your toes to make them so crooked Dad?" "Noh son, I was pulling your leg when I told you that. It's because I broke them playing football with no shoes when we were kids. We often didn't have shoes. It didn't matter in summer. We always knew when summer had come because the spring floods from the River Roding would have gone down and we didn't have to worry about moving the furniture upstairs. Our house was knocked down years ago, about the time when they built these houses, because it flooded so often. Of course we didn't wear shoes in the floods and usually it was still cold then. You could break a toe and not even know till it warmed up in bed; then it'd be sore for weeks. Your uncle and me once had a fight in bed because he'd banged one of my toes that was hurting. That's one reason my toes are crooked.

"Barking still had a wharf when we were kids but the fishing had all gone. All the fish came by train because it was quicker. The wharf was still working but they dealt mainly with timber in barges. It was a rough place. When I was about ten I climbed over a fence, taking a short cut to school and trod on a seaman on the other side. It made me jump, I can tell you. I thought he was dead drunk at first, but then I thought about having trodden on him and realised he wasn't drunk, he was dead. He'd been stabbed.

"In summer we used to swim in the lock at the 'Rushing Waters' below where some of the boats and barges were moored. We could have gone to the municipal pool but you had to pay there and although it might have been clean, it wasn't like swimming in the lock. We used to dare one another to swim under the lock paddle; it was like being flushed down the toilet. They didn't stop us until one or two got stuck and drowned. What was worse, though, was getting typhoid; a few kids got that and then my Dad stopped us going there. He threatened us with his belt. It was two inches wide and made of leather you could have soled your shoes with. He used to scare us with it, whacking it on the stairs.

Barking might be rough now but it was a lot rougher then. The Short Blue pub in North Street was named after a famous fishing smack. That was a rough pub when we were kids, real 'spit and sawdust.' That's where I learnt to play cards." (Dad loved to play cards; bridge, bezique, crib, poker, you name, it Dad played it; he used to win too. He'd remember the cards so it was almost as though he could see through them. He knew how to cheat as well; he knew about marked cards, shaved cards, bending cards - he was an expert.)

"You need to know how they cheat if you're going to catch them. There was always a money-game, at the back of the Short Blue. When I was a kid I used to get tips for keeping dogeye, looking out for the police. The Short Blue was rough, but the Barge Aground was the worst; there were always stabbings and robberies there. Women used to sell themselves, leaning against the back wall, to buy gin. What I remember most about it was the stink. There was the smell of beer and tobacco smoke from the pub, and stale pee. The women used to have split crotch knickers and they'd squat and pee just like the blokes. There were other smells too, even worse, all mixed in. It stank. You didn't go there unless you had to, or wanted trouble. If the police went to that part of town they usually went in twos, on horses, with three-foot long nightsticks - and they'd use 'em.

"There was a cinema nearby called The Broadway Biascope. Us kids used to go there on Saturday mornings. The seats were raked and there was a concrete floor. Some of the kids would pee so it ran down to the front so that stank as well.

"A policeman lived next door to us. He used to get drunk at the weekends and beat his wife up. That wasn't uncommon in those days. They didn't have kids. That was unusual, most couples had loads of kids. Late one night she came to our house scared half to death, she thought he was going to kill her. Your grandfather let her in and Mr Sanger the copper came round and started threatening your grandfather. Your grandad wrote letters for people living in our street because he'd had an education and he threatened to write to the chief of police. Mr Sanger went back home then. His wife left him after that. It wasn't done in those days, leaving your husband. There was only one thing a woman could have done after that. I don't know what happened to her, she just disappeared. It caused lots of gossip for weeks but she never turned up again.

"Things were a lot rougher in those days. Another one of our neighbours went to the pictures and came back with a baby. The woman she went with said it was like shelling peas; she was up and about doing the washing next day. Even when I got older and money wasn't so tight meat porters in the dock were still peeing on one another's backs to toughen up the skin. You could make good money at meat portering but it was a young man's game. You needed to be fit to hump three-hundredweight sides of beef all day. I did some of that in my twenties. I was as fit as a fiddle then, ate like a horse and was as brown as a berry. As you got older, that sort of work was too much.

"A lot of the older blokes had something wrong with them. There was a department they called the 'convalescent home' where the work was lighter and jobs would be found for the older men. You couldn't make the money there but if you had a 'Big 'Un' (that's what they called a hernia) then that's all you could do. If there was a fight it was quite likely they'd use their docker's hooks. If they did, then someone might get maimed or crippled.

Your grandfather was brought up middle class. He was educated till he was nearly sixteen and would have gone to university. Ordinary people couldn't afford an education then. Even the penny a week they used to try to charge was more than people could afford, especially if there were a lot of kids -there was no contraception then. (Your mother'll tell you about that.) Your great grandfather was the stationmaster at Crewe, in charge of over a thousand men. That was a really good job in those days, but he died and the money dried up.

"With the education he'd got, your grandfather managed to get a job with Pearl Assurance. It was just getting going then. He was doing OK but then he was given the boss's son to train. This youth started telling your grandfather what he was and wasn't going to do. Your granddad was proud and stubborn. He wouldn't put up with any of that and made it clear the youth would do as he was told. The young man disagreed and your Grandad knocked him down. That lost him his job and he finished up working as a labourer in the docks.

"Your Grandad's family were military, that's why the Long

Lee Enfield rifle is still over the mantle at your grandfather's. He was in the volunteers. His brother was in the Horse Guards. He was one of their best horsemen. He used to do a circus act standing on his head on his horse, and all sorts of tricks. He was a top act at the Military Tattoos. He made a mistake though. He had an eye for the ladies and he got a bit too close to the C.O's wife, so they sent him to India. He liked a drink and him and three others got drunk, got carried away and the bunch of them kicked a punka wallah (that's one of the blokes who sits and pulls the string that waves the fan) to death. He was up for court martial. We only heard of him a couple of times after that. He went AWOL and skipped to Australia. There were one or two letters as far as I know. He wrote saying he'd become a cowboy and was sitting writing while he stank because he'd not had a bath for two months driving cattle in the outback. Somehow later on, there must have been another letter I suppose, we heard he'd become the mayor of Melbourne or Sidney, one of the big cities, I can't remember which, but if it was true he'd certainly done all right for himself, considering he'd deserted from the army and was due for a court martial."

3

Mum's Tale

My mother spoke of kids with rickets, working ten-hour days and six-and-a -half-day weeks. I wonder if the vision of 'rickety' children wasn't one that haunted her. She had a brother who she favoured but he was crippled and died when he was just twenty. He fell out of his pram as a baby while the elder children were charged with his care. My grandmother didn't find out what had happened until some time after. The children caring for the baby were too frightened and ashamed to tell. By the time my grandmother discovered the truth, the damage was done. The baby's spine was permanently damaged.

I think Mum was one of the children looking after the baby and this awful responsibility weighed on her conscience ever after. She clearly thought big families with insufficient money for the parents to look after the children properly were an indictment of the society she knew as a child.

Mum was completely different from Dad in the way she talked. When I think of her she's often talking in her own graphic way. She could speak verbal silent films even if they were archaic clichés. That sounds like a paradox but listen, really listen to. 'He doesn't know hay from a bull's foot.' Could anyone be more graphically daft? Can you see the bull pawing the ground giving the odd bellow but maybe you've not seen a live bull? So try 'He's like a pig with a musket.' Can you imagine anyone more clumsy? I've heard her say that to Dad more than once. "Give it to me. You're like a pig with a musket," she'd say, raising her eyes to the ceiling in a mixture of disgust and despair at his efforts. He didn't care. It might even have been a trick to get Mum to do something he didn't want to. She could sum up the story of the Second World War, creating a picture that worked, in ten lines and half a dozen facial expressions. There was National Dried Milk for babies, concentrated orange juice for the little ones and free school milk and dinners for all, whatever their income. Mum took nothing on trust and cooked and cleaned like one possessed, determined her children were not going to be visited by the desperation she saw when young. She told me her father took all he could in the way of help.

"He didn't see it as charity, the way your Dad's father did; he thought it was our right. If he was unable to work, it wasn't for the lack of will. It was because they couldn't or wouldn't provide it. We never went without shoes, even when he was out of work. He claimed everything he could from the National Assistance Board, and he didn't go there cap in hand. He went to claim his right and the rights of his children to live like human beings. He did odd jobs whenever he got the

11

chance. He 'worked his loaf' so there was always food, even if it wasn't enough. He was blacklisted for work because he wouldn't put up with insults and knocked a foreman down a hole when he tried to force your grandfather to do a job that wasn't his to do. He was out of work for three years after that. We always got by though, so although we might not have been as posh as your Dad's people, we were really better off because food was more important than pride. Your grandfather knew what was what. He knew what a pound was worth, and when it came to the pinch he always managed to find some money."

Mum didn't talk much about her Dad but she liked and respected him. She used to tell us how he sealed the rooms in their house with tape and burnt sulphur candles and creosoted behind the skirting boards to drive out bed bugs and other vermin. She told me, "You get the nit nurse but when we were kids half the class had nits. If anyone in a family got them, that was it, they all got them, because there were so many of us all crammed into such small spaces. There was contraception but not for ordinary people like us. Marie Stopes did more for working people than all your politicians. She helped make sure contraception was available to everybody."

Of all my relations I liked my mother's father best. I remember him as a small resourceful man who, though he was old, had an air of spriteliness. He still enjoyed life and liked children. He used to make fascinating little toys, whistles and carved sticks to be rubbed with a lolly stick as rhythm instruments. He wore elegant boots that were like shoes but laced up above the ankle; they were light and always well polished and gave him a lively stylish appearance. It wasn't just that his eyes twinkled, there was something elfin about him. He was at ease with himself and always seemed quietly comfortable. He was quick to smile and if you coaxed hard enough he would play a small accordion he called his squeezebox. I liked him to play 'Lord of the Dance' because he played it in a way that matched his personality.

We lived in the city but I always associated him with the hedgerows and lanes where things grew wild, free and untrammelled by all the constrictions that go with buildings, piped water, roads and railways. His family, he said, came from around Kent, Sussex and Hampshire. They were didicois. He sometimes made pegs and other small wooden things using just a sharp knife. He could make baskets though he didn't show me how to do that. There weren't enough willow trees near where we lived. At Christmas he made brushes from odd pieces of wood and horsehair he got from the farriers as well as blackboards and miniature brooms for children's presents.

I could spend hours just poking around in my grandfather's shed amongst oil cans, wood-planes, boxes of junk and tools that were for I knew not what. He was always doing, if he wasn't nodding in his Windsor chair opposite my grandmother, slippered feet warming by the emery polished, steel fender. The door of the black-leaded range stood open, allowing the warm glow of hot coals into the room, whilst the big brown enamelled kettle hissed gently.

Grandad died when he was over seventy, six weeks after coming off a great lump of an old 500 c.c. single cylinder Norton motor bike he'd nursed back to life. He lived his life to the end and nearly died with his boots on, almost as if he'd decided it was time to go.

4

Early Days

At my school the nit nurse came once a term. She was nice and gentle; when she delicately danced her fingers through my hair it gave me lovely shivers. She smiled and gave me barley sugar for not making a fuss when I was immunised against polio. Now and then someone might turn up with great patches stained with purple gentian, for skin problems - scabies, and ringworm but generally speaking we were a healthy lot. Mum used simple nutrition books the government published during the war; that and plenty of exercise kept us fit. The doctor was still a last resort, even though we had the National Health. Lion Ointment came in a cylindrical wooden box with a plain white label with a lion printed in red ink. It smelt of a mixture of sulphur and grease and was used on boils. Boils were more common then. Friars Balsam treated blocked sinuses. It was mixed with hot water in a pastry bowl and you put a tea-towel over your head and breathed in the steam. I really liked the smell; it wasn't so different from cough drops. Last was Vick's vapour rub; it was like Vaseline but you put it up your nose and rubbed it on your chest, it smelt sort of menthol and made your nose feel odd with a sensation crossed between a tingle and anaesthetic. I liked the smell of that too. We only went to the doctor when something serious went wrong, if an arm was broken or when there was a major problem.

We didn't have to fumigate rooms to get rid of bed bugs like our grandparents and hearses weren't loaded six up sideways, with cut sized coffins as children died from diphtheria, whooping cough and scarlet fever epidemics partly because of malnutrition. Dad nearly died of diphtheria when he was about three and said he could remember hearses stopping along the street to collect small coffins. He was funny about food because he knew what it was to starve. TB was still a threat and to become victim might still lead to ostracism brought on by unreasoning fear. Now it's HIV.

The culture in Dagenham was simple; most houses were well cared for. The baths and inside toilets were regarded by tenants as wonderful luxuries, not used to store coal, an outcome predicted by some of letting the 'the great unwashed' loose with such facilities. There was irony to that. The houses were designed with a coal cupboard under the stairs. Nobody wanted coal in the house. It caused too much dirt and dust, but there was no outside passage to the back garden and dirty booted coalmen tramped through the houses twice a year (more if the family used the tallyman) to shoot coal into a bunker in the garden. Had the designers of the houses abandoned their prejudices and imagined themselves in the shoes of the tenants, they'd have included some outside access to the backs. We, like most others, used the coal cupboard, scrubbed clean and whitewashed, to store the vacuum cleaner, ironing board and other domestic odds and ends.

The chimney sweep usually came once a year in the spring. His visit was anticipated with dismay. Everything was moved as far from the fireplaces as possible and covered as well as might be. Carpets were rolled and wedged and covered with newspaper. The sweep covered the hearth with a dirty black cloth and I was sent to watch for the brush issuing from the chimney, wriggling and dancing like a no-armed puppet. It was my duty to bang on the window to indicate to the sooty-faced man that his brush had appeared and could make its return journey, dislodging its unwelcome billowing black clouds into our hearth and living-room. Some soot was kept to build around celery to keep the stalks white and sweet. Celery today is tough stringy stuff in taste and texture next to the delicate white sticks we grew banked with soot from the chimney.

Sometimes chimneys caught fire. Some of the more disreputable tenants lit them on purpose, stuffing paraffin soaked newspaper up the chimney and setting it on fire. Then the neighbours would come out to ooh and ah at the spectacle as red-blue flames leapt roaring and spitting into a shivering heat haze, patterned with white hot sparks that rose and fell in a fountain more exciting than a Guy Fawkes Roman Candle. Salt was thrown into the hearth. It was said to quell the flames. Then yellowish white smoke issued forth. It seldom worked but it added to the drama before the fire brigade was called to do the work of the sweep. The results can't have been worth the trouble. Mum saw the perpetrators of this trick as foolish and unworthy and sent them to Coventry in a personal crusade. I could imagine her Dad knowing ways to stop the mess. If he had, he'd have smiled and given a merry wink, laughing gently at his straight-laced daughter.

The council did its best and competitions were held for the best-kept gardens; some were really beautiful. There was competition among tenants themselves to keep the houses well, using the standards set by those who had been 'In service' to the wealthy before the war. Lots of scrubbing, polishing and diligent work was the order of the day with 'elbow grease' held in high esteem.

Dagenham people had mostly lived through the war. Some tried evacuation, to find themselves facing squalor reminiscent of the slums so recently escaped. Many returned, preferring to take their chance with the bombs. There was a crack in one of the doors at home that was pointed out to visitors as a trophy from a landmine that exploded a quarter of a mile away. Our cracked door was one of the few signs of damage apart from the gap left where half a dozen houses were flattened.

5

Bombs, Mr Tizzard and Christmas Pudding

Mr Tizzard, a bus driver, who lived two doors away, built a big smart garage for his little Standard Eight car. It was really well done and people agreed he was clever for having made such a good job. Mum didn't approve; she thought it was too big and ruined the country feel of the big square of back gardens, spoiling the view of trees and plants. She respected Mr Tizzard though and acknowledged that he was a local hero for having been expert at throwing incendiary bombs back out through the holes they punched through roofs during the war. That was truly dangerous because the bombs might explode into incandescent white heat at any moment. The only way to control an incendiary fire was cover it with sand until the thing burnt out, by which time it might have gone through several floors to reach the ground. Occasionally an unexploded bomb or shell would turn up when people were digging, providing an exciting reason to recount hair-raising tales of land mines dangling on taut threads of entangled parachutes, or the tense wait through the pregnant silence when a doodlebug's engine stopped, the tale ending with the horrifying whistle, building to a crescendo and culminating in the explosion that might signal the terrified listener's path to oblivion.

When it was hot we kids played, squirting one another with the stirrup pump issued by the government to control fires during the war. I never heard of one used to control a fire. Gas masks were never used either. We played Martians with them, but not often; they were too uncomfortable. Voices from within them were muffled, making it difficult to hear, nor could hints of words be gleaned through moving lips. Mum used to complain, saying they'd have been better spending the money on something useful like decorating or food.

As well as migrants from London's East End, there were lots of Irish and Scots, with a good sprinkling of other nationalities, giving a kind of vibrancy to life here not found with older more stable populations elsewhere. There was an air of optimism around. The war was over and things were getting sorted out. The bombsites that made East London's skyline ragged, like the smile of a grey-faced gap-toothed crone, were being built over or used as parks for the cars churned out at Fords. For once a Tory was right. Macmillan said, 'You've never had it so good' - it was true and it's gonna get better still - or else - was the mood. Some of the Irish still talked of the time when they started at Fords and of the house near the factory gate where all the rooms were full of beds that were never cold because they were used on a three shift system to match the factory's. The landlady was well known for making porridge in the copper designed for doing washing.

Mum did something similar. As part of the Christmas ritual she used our copper to make Christmas puddings for several neighbours. I had to wish while stirring the mixture in a big wash-bowl before it went into nine basins to be covered with greaseproof paper, carefully tied on with white cotton string that nipped my finger while I held the knot as Mum pulled it tight, prior to stacking the basins in the copper, three to a tier, in three tiers, with boards in between. The cooking began and condensation and the delicious smell of Christmas pudding permeated the house, while I filled with anticipation for pudding and everything else that went with Christmas as they steamed for hours. Hmmm.

6

Poverty Gone, Brave new World
& Death of Victorian England

My earliest memories are of a nursery, an innovation of a government intent on building a 'Brave New World'. It could hardly be worse than the poverty of pre-war England.

There was some tension in our house because my mother had been,not just the only female manager in a small chain of grocery shops, but also the youngest and when she married my father she felt deprived of the satisfaction the job gave her, especially after they offered her incentives to stay. More than once she told me about the canteen of cutlery her employers gave as a wedding present.

"That's a good set, Viners - not many people round here have anything as good as that. When we were married most cutlery was still made of ordinary steel. This is stainless and they're best bone handles. Twenty years old and look, good as new, and the spoons and forks are best quality EPNS thick nickel silver, none of your thin cheap coatings. It's almost as good as the real thing and you couldn't expect them to give real silver. I don't suppose even they've got that on the table. Our best wedding present it was. They wanted me to stay, even offered me part time, but your Dad wasn't having any of that. I married him and he wasn't having any "part time"; he was going to provide for his family the way a real man should. Expected his dinner on the table when he got in, so now you're used to having the table laid properly when we eat. Next door they think we act like royalty here just because we lay the table properly."

At mealtimes we all ate together with the table properly laid with a white damask, smooth, ironed table cloth. We didn't start until all hands were washed and when we finished us kids had to ask. "Please can I get down?"

Dad harboured a stereotyped image of himself as a Victorian style breadwinner; following his father as a staunch self-respecting man in his own house. Did Mum too dream of a 'Brave New World' where women were something other than housewives? She'd lost her economic independence, unlike many women who continued to work after the war. She was torn between wanting to do the right thing by her family and at the same time wondering if personal ambition and fulfilment, and commitment to family might not be mutually exclusive.

She chose total commitment to the family, cleaning and cooking, obsessive, almost self-destructive. Our front step was always the best scrubbed. The bedsheets on her washing-line were always the whitest and this determination to be the most committed housewife continued indoors. Monday was washing day when sheets were boiled in the copper and the house filled with the horrible smell of damp cotton and verdigris heated with coal gas. Bed-sheets were changed and ironed weekly, floors polished, ceilings dusted and nooks and crannies sought out for treatment. Our house was spotless. When the cooker was twenty years old a salesman called, aiming to sell Mum a new one. She let him in to see the old one. He was astounded at its 'as new' condition. He departed, saying, "You're right lady. I can't sell you anything that's going to last as well as that." The cooker had been religiously cleaned each day for twenty years. She knitted and sewed, making do and mending with the best. Don't misunderstand, she was still approachable as a person.

I'll always remember the first time I heard her swear. It was a lovely sunny day with a 'good drying breeze'. She'd just washed the sheets and pegged them on the washing-line when a large bird, unable to resist the temptation of such a great expanse of pure white, sent a huge splat right across a bright, white sheet. Mother doggedly lowered the line, jaw set rigid. With close-mouthed, determined patience the sheet was taken in, rewashed, and again pegged out and the line raised again to catch the best of the drying wind. Mum wasn't big, but she could pull her weight all right and gave a final tug on the line, to vent her frustration when twang! it snapped... Mum slowly turned, stood, folded her arms, then, surveying her wonderfully clean line of washing laid on the dusty ground, she breathed in hard and with a forced outward breath said one word, embodying all the boiling anger within: "Shit."

I kept out of the way, all too aware that to stay close was to risk becoming the butt of her bubbling anger. It took time before she could laugh about that day, but eventually she did. She could laugh at herself. I didn't hear my Dad swear till much later, although we all knew that he did because Mum used 'dockology' (He was a foreman in the dock) as a euphemism for swearing. He arrived late from work, on his bike, cold, wet, and caked in snow. Mum said. "Oh, is it snowing?" Dad's reflexive reply was. "Snowin'... it's a fuckin' blizzard."

I hid, for fear I'd laugh. It was all I could do to suppress my giggles. Swearing was still taboo, but the walls of convention were cracking.

7

Nursery Days

My nursery teacher had a lot of dark shoulder-length hair, worn loose. She dressed in light coloured two-piece, suits, and wore vivid red lipstick. She was alien, scary.

Mum liked good perfume; Yardley's Lavender was always a safe bet for a present. Toilet water if you were feeling mean, and real perfume if you were flush, but lipstick was for high days and holidays. Powder and paint during the week was for tarts and the upper classes with nothing better to do than idle around all day, dolled up to the nines, ordering people about who did the real work.

In the mornings we played with toys. We played on the classroom floor of dark polished parquet. It was dusty so as you moved about clothes acted as mops, picking up dust and a smell of polished parquet. There wasn't much cash for toys at home and I'd already played using a cheap hammer bought for the odd occasion when Dad couldn't wriggle out of carrying out some minor domestic 'do-it-yourself' task. I used it for bashing sticks into the lumpy clay soil of our garden. At the nursery in a battered and scratched plywood box was a toy wooden frame. It was stained bright colours and designed with shaped holes, through which sprung pegs were knocked with a small mallet as an exercise in co-ordination, I guess. I'd already learned this lesson from the hammer in the garden. It was imprinted on my brain at the cost of floods of tears and a dark blue fingernail that fascinated me as it grew to click, as I flapped it, and eventually fell off. I liked this toy and knocked the pegs with such gusto that the frame broke. I think I probably made a terrible row into the bargain.

My first brush with authority followed. Trouble. I don't remember the outcome but events took a turn for the worse. By the end of my first week another child had whacked me over the head with a chair. The chairs were small but the blow was enough to knock me senseless. All I remember is waking in bed at home concussed and puking over the bedclothes. More trouble. The nursery staff came in for flack too - a pointed interview with my disgruntled parents.

I must have settled in after that because the only other thing I recall about the nursery was being expected to sleep on canvas folding beds with itchy grey blankets that looked like army surplus camping equipment and smelled musty. Each afternoon everything suddenly stopped while beds were unfolded, blankets distributed, then all us kids were instructed to sleep - switch off... 'click'... sleep to order. I

21

remember giggling and feigning sleep while making silly noises when the teacher's back was turned. Did those deciding our curriculum know 'hay from a bull's foot?'

❧ ❧ ❧ ❧

8

Images

Outside the nursery, childhood is remembered as a series of images rather than events. I hold a wrinkled apple to feed to the milkman's horse whilst mum says, 'Hold your hand out flat and he won't bite. Horses like apples, not little boys. He won't bite. He just wants the apple.'

Little was wasted and there was method in the madness of sacrificing even a wrinkled old apple. It was a ploy. It was the sort of thing her Dad would have done. The hope was that the excitement of a stop in the incessant plodding and pulling the milk cart and joy at the treat of an apple would cause the horse to empty its bowels. Being on the spot we would have first claim on the steaming heap, for use as fertilizer in the garden. I was encouraged to carefully watch the milkman's horse in the hope it would produce a pile. If fortune smiled and dobbin deposited his unwanted load, my job was to pounce, ahead of the neighbours, bucket and shovel at the ready, to collect the wonderful bounty.

My mother loved her garden - daffodils, crocus and primulas in spring; roses, stocks and flox; golden rod and hollyhocks through the summer. Autumn saw the lawn fed, trimmed, raked and forked. In winter bonemeal, lime and dried blood and compost were scattered. No effort was spared. She read books from the library. She knew most of the Latin names of the plants. She layered, took cuttings and

22

even attempted grafting, though I think with little success. She was shameless about chatting to people she wasn't even acquainted with, intent on arranging a plant swop. A pink for a peony tuber, or better, something exotic, a bay tree cutting or a Christmas rose.

The garden only became a true garden after I'd started at the nursery. Before that, it was accepted that we kids could use it as a playground without restriction, apart, of course, from fighting. We had at least one tricycle that mum's Dad made up from various odds and ends of scrap. I rode madly around on the hard packed dusty clay of our 'garden' determined to get onto two wheels on the bends. We played shops using discarded soap powder and other packets. Grass was green beans and stones served as potatoes. Arguments degenerating into violence might result in slapped legs, or even worse, enforced sitting quietly bickering in the 'living room' till Dad's dreaded arrival when, after explanations from my mother we sat downcast and apologetic, waiting to discover our frightening fate. The wait was invariably worse than the punishment.

I was allocated a square yard of soil, given some seeds and shown how to plant them. I can remember today my delight at seeing the first tiny leaves peeping from the avidly watched, too often poked, carefully watered soil as my first crop of sweet peas followed by delphiniums grew daily to finally burst into glorious flower, bringing a great feeling of achievement.

Basic to the establishment of the garden was the laying of a path up to the post that supported the washing line. Dad was the most impractical of men but physically strong, active and willing. The digging out for a foundation was done, shuttering boards fitted, hardcore dumped, and cement mixed. It should have been concrete but Dad wasn't aware there was any difference between mortar and concrete. Cement was cement to Dad. The mix may have been over expensive and wrong but the result was serviceable and smooth if a little undulating.

9

Something Bad Happened

I was three years old. It was sudden. Something bad happened. I knew because late at night our neighbour was woken to 'see' to us kids. There was an ambulance, I don't remember it. I do remember the atmosphere. Everything was subdued. I didn't know why. Come the morning the porridge our neighbour made didn't taste right and it was sprinkled with sugar that crunched as you chewed, instead of syrup. Nothing was right and then we went to the hospital. The first time, we weren't allowed in. In those days patients slept in the open (part of the cure for TB). Dad's bed was pointed out by a finger indicating a first or second floor balcony veranda. 'Wave'. Do I remember him waving back? Later we visited and he was allowed to come to the black painted iron railings surrounding the hospital grounds. He wore slippers in among the leaves covering the grass and pyjamas under a dull, grey, purple, and blue, plaid dressing gown, something I'd never seen before.

He'd suffered a burst stomach ulcer and nearly died. It was an awful time for my mother. She used to recount the events of the night, telling us with flushed face and tears latent in her eyes, that she went off to the hospital in the ambulance with my father, wearing a coat over her nightdress. When he'd been admitted she was sent from the hospital in Romford with just the bus-fare home. She had to catch the bus from the poorly lit stop at the hospital gate, late at night, still wearing the coat over her bloodied nightdress. I knew by the way she told the story that the journey scarred her mind for life.

It wasn't till much later that I realised how horrible that night was for her. I was too young. I just had an impression of it being a quiet, solemn time when arguing and fighting with my sister couldn't be. We had to be quiet. Things were bad. Apart from that I was too small for it to really mean much.

Recollections come haphazardly. I remember at junior school rationing was still in force. I've heard since that sweets and sugar were scarcer than during the war. When a lorry rolled onto its side at the top of our street there was a near riot as the rumour spread that it was carrying sugar and all you needed was a bucket and shovel. I've no idea how much of its cargo was rescued by the authorities but I'm sure a whole lot went missing. It was a day remembered with fond nostalgia, the Dagenham equivalent of *Whiskey Galore*.

෴෴෴

10

Christmas

At Christmas we would circulate around relatives, usually Dad's brothers. They lived within walking distance. Starting at a pre-arranged house on the first evening and then on, first to one of my uncles, then to the next over three evenings. We played with our new toys with our cousins. There would be the traditional meal at lunchtime, at home with just our family, and later in the evening we all met at one house for party games, holiday camp style, passing balloons between knees and fishing jam covered apples from bowls of water with only teeth allowed to grip.

There were oranges, still a delicacy in those post-war days. A grey calf length sock, doubled as a stocking. The orange would always be at the bottom, turning the thing into a Raymond Chandler style cosh, ideal for swinging. 'Don't swing that or you'll break something.' Why was it always so swingable?

There would be other odds and ends, 'stocking fillers' my mother called them, some nuts and small toys: one of those puzzles, a miniature maze with a tiny ball-bearing or blob of mercury to be manipulated to the centre, or a wooden puzzle from Japan that made into the shape of an elephant, duck or cube that was easy to get apart but oh so difficult to put together again.

There was always booze for the adults. The women would be expected to drink sherry or port, with the younger ones drinking 'Cherry B' or 'Snowballs' made with Advocaat and lemonade. If they were lucky and Dad 'in the money' there might be Cherry Brandy, Drambuie or Tia Maria. Dad and my uncles would get tipsy and tell stories of Christmases past. There would be the tale of the time when Grandfather was out of work and uncle found a ten-shilling note that paid for kippers for Christmas dinner.

There was the story about rice pudding when grandfather asked "Who likes skin?" and someone said, "Ooh skin, I love the skin." Then he asked "Who likes corners?" and a couple said, "Me, I like corners." Then uncle said "I like it all", to which grandfather replied "Right, half for you and half for me cos' the rest aren't really hungry."

Dads' father was a terrible, Victorian despot. Sometimes, out would come photos and there he'd be. "All dolled up like a dogs dinner," Mum would say, "with spats, silver topped cane, bowler and kid gloves and big fat moustache waxed at the ends." He used to twist the ends saying, 'Waxed with the green end of a duck's turd.' What a terrible man.

Worries were forgotten and life was fun for a few days but even so 'Big Presents' usually had a practical value - tools, books or a bike to save bus fares. Even though we weren't religious people we actually lived like ardent puritans. Nothing wasted, and hard work revered. Sam Smiles and *Self Help* still ruled in our house.

11

Mum and Dad Together

Relationships within marriage were different fifty years ago. My Mum and Dad were closer than most. They must have been; I don't ever remember them rowing. They married quite late. My mother told me that she'd been resigned to the idea of never being married. As the eldest daughter I think that she probably took quite a good deal of responsibility for running the home even when she was working and financially independent.

They met on a holiday day trip. There are photographs somewhere of Mum near the front of a group holding a Japanese painted parasol, with other young women, and Dad looking jaunty with young men at the back. All were dressed ready for a walk on the prom', short sleeves, flannels and summer dresses. Dad must have been keen because he was regarded as something of a 'catch', I'm led to believe. Mum never mentioned any other suitors, though I'm sure there were some. There were times when she explained how she dealt with the unwanted attention of men in the shop where she worked, encountering what today would be called sexual harassment. She wasn't frightened to defend herself. She told me that if she went to the pictures (that may be cinema to you) she wore a hat with a good big hatpin and used it on at least one occasion with some relish. "Stuck it in his leg. I think it was his leg," grinning and raising her eyebrows. "Three inches long it was, with a nice big knob on top to get hold of. He didn't yell, but it stopped him in his tracks, I can tell you. Didn't even stay to the end of the film. Serve him right - pig."

I've no idea what resistance Dad met; I only know the outcome. The wedding was the whole thing, white dress, bridesmaids, big cake, church, the lot. Dad would have wanted that, he liked to put on a show.

I don't remember them arguing, though I'm sure they must have. Mum always wanted a quiet life and she couldn't have been more dutiful. Dad was intensely loyal. I think he'd have defended any of us beyond the bounds of reason. 'Family first' might have been his motto. Women and children were to be treated honourably in all circumstances, even if they were a pain in the neck. He always raised his hat to ladies and dressed to look tidy if not smart. Within the bounds of the family you did as you were told or suffered the consequences. Mum, I think, saw her place as being subservient though there must have been times when it rankled. Dad always set out to give the impression he wasn't afraid of anything. In physical terms this may have been largely true. He did go in fear of losing his job though. He liked to have money in his pocket and give the impression that he was better off than he really was. It was Mum who suffered as a result. Money was tight and she resented his going to the pub on Saturday lunchtimes and sometimes coming late for the meal though I don't suppose he spent a great deal. That was how families managed in those days otherwise people would have lived too much in each other's pockets. The pressure would have been unendurable. Wife beating was common as it was, and there were many more blind eyes cast. Dad would never have laid a finger on my mother and he'd have defended her to the last breath. I think that meant a lot to her. No doubt things were tough at times but as I said, they got on better than most. They made their marriage work as an act of duty. There must have been disagreements but I never knew.

They both did their best. Dad provided, but was a little humanly selfish at times. Mum did her job almost too conscientiously. Good food on the table was always the first concern. One of her favourite sayings was 'Huh, pride, poverty and pianners.' This dismissed those living above their means. She regarded anyone resorting to tally men and buying on the 'Never' as the worst kind of fools, almost criminally irresponsible. 'Better to eat off orange boxes and drink from jam jars than buy on the 'Never'. She was a cash customer or no customer at all.

Holidays and Antimacassars

As I grew older there was money for holidays. The first I remember was when we went to Littlehampton and spent a week at a boarding house. It wasn't a success. The food didn't meet the exacting standards of my parents. Mum simply thought it was poor and my father who was a bit cranky about what he ate, especially since his burst ulcer, was less than impressed,
"I'll never touch another boiled chicken and you can keep haddock steamed in milk too." He couldn't have his regular pint of beer with the main meal either. (He didn't stick to the diet laid down by the hospital for long). He wasn't an alcoholic by any means. I only saw him anything like drunk two or three times but a main meal without beer as an aperitif was almost inconceivable.

We went on a steam train. The tube was commonplace, there was a Metropolitan Line station a ten-minute walk from our house and sometimes we'd go by train in preference to the bus but a steam train was new. A steam train meant real travel, far away, further than I'd ever been. Tube trains must have been much lighter than steam engines because the memory of the platform rumbling and vibrating as the train arrived mighty and portentous made a lasting impression. This was a majestic leviathan, hissing and bubbling steam, filling the air with coal smoke and the smell of boiled oil, a dragon on wheels, breathing excitement and drama. The carriages were so different from the humdrum dust, sweat and tobacco odours of the 'Tube,' ingrained with smells of woollen cloth, polish and lino'. The station itself was imposing; a cathedral to travel, with a continuous stream of people, paths criss-crossing, all alert, intent on different destinations. Not like our local tube station, a shabby, brick and tarmac parochial church to commuting where people went to or from work like automatons so that the two platforms saw bursts of activity that could have been rehearsals for the real thing, then subsided into somnolence as trains came and went.

I was intrigued by the antimacassars on the headrests of the seats in the first class compartments. I asked "What are the white things for?" "They're antimacassars to stop Brylcream from staining the seats.""Why are they called antimacassars?" "They used to use Macassar oil before Brylcreem." The name Macassar oil blended with my image of the steam train, rich, foreign, exotic and mysterious, while Brylcreem said Metropolitan Line. Everything was so different from the tube, most of all the people themselves. Even to my young eyes many were unlike the people of Dagenham. Their clothes, their air, so much more assured, relaxed and comfortable with their places in the world and on such a train.

We had to write about our holiday when I went back to school and I wrote about the train journey. I was unhappy when I was marked down for writing about the journey and not the holiday. The journey was the holiday for me. On the way back I talked to another lad as we passed through Havant, both dejected at the prospect of returning home. With a dreamy look at the signboard on the station he said quietly, "Havant...haven't any money." I've seldom felt more in sympathy with another person than I felt with that lad then, as the train tumety tum, tumety tummed, lurching and swaying towards the uninspiring ordinariness of home 'Me neither and school next week.' I thought.

I felt this, even though I didn't like the boarding house. I agreed with my parents. The food was better at home and the building had an unfamiliar smell that I didn't like, that smell still conjures visions of musty, brown varnished, lincrusta wallpaper, old fry-ups and dusty pile flattened carpets, with dull patterns, too long in ill lit, high-ceilinged old-fashioned rooms. Added to that I had to be quiet all the time for the horse-faced landlady whose disapproving looks turned ugly when I had the temerity to talk. She was just like the hatchet faced librarian at home who stamped our books as though she was releasing us from prison and glowered at us if we so much as whispered.

On the other hand there was the elementally different, wide-open sea, infinite with specks of ships and yachts imperceptibly moving on a warm inviting horizon; salty sea winds laced with smells of rotting seaweed and whispering waves receding to the shivering rattle of glistening pebbles on wet sand that rode up through the toes with a sensation like no other; and above all premonitions of the unexpected and adventure.

There were unforgettable moments, as when we sat enjoying the warm sunshine among ice cream booths and beach huts with the restrained hubbub of distant squeals from the beach and "Rub some lotion on my back", "Where's the beach ball?" "Don't use that towel, You'll get it all sandy". Waiting to go into the lido, my memory is hazy, of a scene, bright, like one of those pointillist pictures with people sitting in groups and couples close together on rich, green, tidily mown, municipal grass. There wasn't much space. A couple nearby were ardently kissing and cuddling. People stared, disapproving. The pair, careless of their public situation, carried by instinct beyond sensibility, he using his jacket to hide them as their movements developed a rhythm. Only half understanding what was going on but intuitively sensing the shocked indignation of all the adults around, I was enthralled.

A man in dark uniform strode up, straight and un-compromising, and with casual aplomb unceremoniously doused the pair with a bucket of water, turning coolly to march purposefully away, to voices of approval and even clapping from righteously indignant watchers. What a show, a highlight of the holiday. I remember my parent's grim, prim, approval. "Huh, act like dogs and they should be treated like dogs."

Speaking of dogs and their doings, I glanced down and glittering in the sun lay a coin, then another and another, a treasure trove, just in the right place, by the sea, in the land of pirates and smugglers. Someone, distracted by the spectacle while lying in the grass, had risen, failing to notice the contents of their back pocket shed in a glorious bounty for my quick fingers to retrieve in joyful excitement. How much I collected I've no idea but it was enough to make the day even more memorable.

೪೪೪೪

13

Boxing

Holidays and weekends were the only times I had much to do with my father. In the week he got up at about six for breakfast and a wash and shave, to be ready for the five mile bike ride to work. In the evening he arrived home at about six. By the time he'd eaten tea it was nearly bed time for me, and having done a day's work and ridden ten miles on his bike he had little energy left for time with the family. On Saturday afternoons (he usually worked in the mornings) he sometimes took us (me and the younger of my two sisters) to watch his beloved football at Barking, where I would sit on the perimeter wall with the week's treat, a bag of peanuts still in their shells. The stands would be littered with peanut shells after a game. (Now they're under a shopping mall). He loved physical games and had been quite a sportsman in his day.

In my parents' bedroom, on top of Dad's wardrobe, stood a cup that may have been solid silver, it was certainly silver-plated. Raised on its bakelite plinth, it fascinated me, I don't know why. Occasionally I was given the job of polishing it with 'Brasso' and a piece of old woollen sock. It wasn't a penance; I enjoyed it. The dining table was prepared carefully with a covering of newspaper. I remember the 'Brasso' smell as it came from the tin and how it changed as the wool became impregnated with the silver oxide while I watched the black tarnish disappear as I rubbed. The cup was a 'dust harbourer,' according to my mother and knew what it was to fly. It was almost as battered as if it had spent a quarter of an hour bouncing around in a cement mixer. Mum's dusters were wild things. It's occurred to me since that they were a means to vent her frustration at being constricted by the society of the day. Dad must have been proud of the cup, for it to stand where it did. Whether it annoyed him to see it so battered, I've no idea. He had other cups and medals for boxing, football and maybe tennis but the one on top of the wardrobe was clearly the most highly prized. I think it was for football. I thought it sad that Mum treated it with such casual disregard, and wondered if there was some undisclosed reason.

I believe I was a bit of a disappointment to my Dad because although I was quite athletic I wasn't particularly interested in sporty things not, as they put on CV's these days, a team player. He had, what now seems to me to be, a sort of 'Boys Own' view of sport. Not to be interested was pansyish; not quite manly; not that he thought I was homosexual, just not quite hundred percent. He did his best to hide his feelings, but without success. My interest in things mechanical was anathema to my father. Riding motorbikes was okay but he couldn't think of anything less interesting than tinkering with them. I felt that way about sport. His favourite pastimes were cross-words and cards, neither of which did a great deal for me. He tried to be supportive but our interests were so different we simply didn't as-you-might-say, jell.

My secondary school was the home of Barking Boxing Club. Dad encouraged me to box. "It's a good thing to be able to look after yourself," he used to say. I didn't thank him, but he wasn't wrong.

He fought his brother for the championship of the docks. He was still surprisingly fit at fifty-three. We went to a Port of London sports day and he entered for the veterans' hundred yards. I've got short legs and he was the same but I'd never seen him move the way he did that day. His legs were short but they spun like Catherine wheels and he won by a convincing couple of yards, despite running against forty year olds.

I didn't enjoy boxing. We had to train. I quite enjoyed skipping but sparring was another matter. For that, I had to wear boxing gloves. Nowadays boxing gloves are simple things, a bit leathery smelling but nothing of any real consequence beyond, perhaps, what they represent. The gloves we wore were something different; already wet, heavy and stinking with other people's sweat. My hands slipped inside as if entering a cold, rotten little carcass. I still shiver at the thought.

When it came to actual fighting, I'd be scared stiff, chattering and giggling nervously to hide my fear. In the first round I'd get hit as I tried to keep out of the way. By the end of the round, though, I'd be mad enough to want to hit back and I had learnt how to punch. I think perhaps part of the reason I won was because during the first round my opponents were convinced I was a pushover. At the start of the second I'd forgotten my fear and came out determined to give as good as I got. We were well taught and I knew I must keep my head and watch my opponent's eyes. "Remember, read their eyes and you can see their next move. Always read their eyes. Punch straight and lock your whole body into a punch; twist your arm as you punch - that'll split the skin of the face. Let him swing haymakers, the more the better. Nothing'll wear him out quicker. Keep your punches short and straight; it'll use less energy and as long as your body's behind them they'll do the job. Try to wet the gloves, that makes them stickier, better for splitting skin. Get your head on the side away from the referee and use it." This is sport?

Our trainer was an ex-professional with a flattened nose and shiny white scar tissue for eyebrows. He'd worked the fairgrounds taking on all comers and at fifty was still alert so he must have been good. Occasionally an old crony would turn up who'd not been so good, their sluggish bodies and slow, slurred speech a testament to failure. He thought we should all wash our hands and faces in urine. "Toughens the skin better than vinegar," was his advice. He could remember the days just after bare knuckles when gloves were so light they meant little and it was accepted that fighters sometimes died or were maimed. He said it might be a good idea to drink urine. "If it works on the outside?" Opponents previously lulled into a false sense of security in round one discovered in round two I could punch with either hand.

My boxing career ended when I was thirteen. I'd got to the quarterfinals of the Dagenham Boys' Tournament. It was held at Barking Swimming Pool. In the winter the pool was covered over and dances, boxing matches and other events were held. The floor boomed like a kettledrum as I skipped in the ring and the bare walls bounced the shouts of the crowd. I was enveloped in noise, accentuating my self-consciousness and fear. With the fear came a kind of exhilaration and a feeling that a part of me was outside my body looking down on the hall, as though watching a film. I won two fights to get to the final, by which time I was gasping, tired and my left eye was closed with a 'mouse'. Then I was expected to meet another opponent who'd had one easy fight; his other had been a 'walkover'. I was past caring by then. I knocked him down three times and he knocked me down once. I had no idea whether I'd won or lost. Seconds mashed into a timeless vacuum. I stood because I was programmed to and punched even though my arms thought the gloves were made of wet concrete. I didn't think. I existed.

Fifteen seconds from the end the referee stopped the fight in favour of my opponent because I had a 'mouse' under my left eye. The referee was my opponent's teacher. My father was disgusted. I was delighted. I never boxed again. The club was nationally known but went out of fashion when one of its stars, an ABA Champion, a tall thin lad, whose knock-out punch was said to be like a jab from a broom handle, met a stocky youth who got inside his lethal long left and produced an uppercut that burst his spleen. Three days later he died. He was twenty.

***

Dad accepted I'd more or less grown up when I was fifteen. We were working making a cupboard for the kitchen. Dad who despised that sort of thing, was hammering nails with all the aptitude of a boozy

35

navvy attempting a belly dance. I counted his strokes waiting for the blow that would hit his finger. Mum's Dad could have played a rising crescendo on his squeezebox with a wicked sparkle in his eye before the inevitable happened. When it came I couldn't help laughing. He reflexively struck out sending my glasses flying.

I stepped across the room, picked them up and said. "Now look what you've done. You've bent my glasses." I was still half laughing at the, time regardless of my sore nose. The fact that my glasses now sat crookedly on my nose distorting my vision made the episode even funnier. Not long after that incident, Dad and I went to the pub together. We'd accepted each other for what we were and from then on got on better than ever before. It wasn't till later I realised that the way we thought was altogether different. It didn't emerge till quite a lot later, when we started talking politics. I'd never understood how my father reached his conclusions until it slowly it dawned on me he didn't. Nothing was ever conclusive for him because he based his opinions on a series of traditional prejudices and stereotypes. I have an idea that his understanding of the world was based in patterns that moved around like bits of coloured glass in a kaleidoscope.

"Why do you vote labour, Dad?"

"Because it's the party of the working man, son."

"But some of their policies don't seem to favour working men?"

"Ah, that's because they have to make compromises, even with the bosses. They have to make a living too."

"But some of them are making a lot more than a living."

"Ah, but there's loyalty. Without loyalty no-one can depend on anyone."

"Yeh but is it sense to be loyal to someone who's tricking you?"

"You've still got to make compromises, that's what compromises are all about."

"So compromises are about making compromises?"

"Don't talk silly, you know what I mean." - beginning to get

36

annoyed. At this point I usually gave up because Mum would be getting flustered at the thought of friction. If I felt bloody-minded, I'd keep going.

"I'm not being silly. I don't know what you mean" Then he'd really start to get annoyed, huffing and puffing and talking real nonsense. I just gave up in the end and let him get on with his pointless crossword puzzles. 'P blank SS blank blank G, A dog with two tails? Oh, that's easy,' whiling away his hours in what, to me, was a way of occupying time as he waited to die.

14

Mum and Alf Garnett

Mum was different altogether. She summed up her ideas in clichés and one-liners "Homes Fit for Heroes, that's what Lloyd–George promised after the First World War and what did we get? Two million unemployed, that's what. Work? There was no work. 'You work to live, you don't live to work.' If there's no work, then what do you do? Go begging or down the N.A.B. (National Assistance Board). You can say what you like about Hitler; at least he gave them work. They built roads as well as bombs. What did they do here? paid a shilling a day for digging holes and filling them up again, rain or shine, in boots with holes to match and clothes falling off you, they were so worn out. That's what it was like for your grandfather. They hoped people would die of pneumonia so they wouldn't have to keep paying the dole. If it hadn't been for the war, we'd all be dead. We'd have starved to death. They built these houses because they knew they had to do something or there'd have been a revolution like in Russia. Chamberlain? 'Peace in our time'? Huh just baiting Hitler and biding time while they got ready for the second lot. 'Peace in our time, Huh'. Chamberlain didn't have to put up with the bombs."

She came up with a structured analysis. Even if it wasn't well informed she looked at the facts as she knew them and achieved a reasoned result. She'd only come out with this sort of stuff when Dad wasn't there because she simply wouldn't argue with him, partly, I think, because there was no discussing with Dad. If you didn't agree with him, you were in for an argument and he was **not** wrong, though I once argued with him long enough for him to change his opinion to the complete opposite from the one he started with, without realising what he'd done. Stubborn like his father - there's a streak of that in me too. I can't help thinking of 'Alf Garnett' when I think of Dad and politics.

15

Spec's, Bugs, Tiddlers & Microscopes

I was about nine when we used to go fishing for tiddlers in the gravel pits, known locally as Matchstick Island, goodness knows where the name came from. There had been plans to turn the area into a smart park but the war put a stop to that, the place was a mess. Its centre was dominated by a two-storey building designed as a pavilion. It had never been completed and, after twenty years of kids doing all the awful things kids do in empty buildings, its windows were clad in galvanised sheet steel and part of its roof was gone, showing charcoal black, skeletal remains of trusses. On three sides were verandas covering areas set back from the frontage. Corners were soot streaked, black from illicit camp fires. All around, big nail-scratched, graffitied brick pillars supported joists of pergolas. The whole area smelt like an ancient cave, desecrated with the sharp ammonia stink of dried pee, but it served as a perfect spot for hide-and-seek.

For us kids, 'Matchy' was a wonderfully dangerous adventure playground. We had great fun there, playing games that transformed it into the Wild West or Klondike, or simply somewhere where we could play like young animals, revelling joyfully in getting filthy and smelly from paddling in the stagnant pools where stickle backs, tadpoles and water boatmen could be pursued, captured, examined and collected in jars as trophies, to be returned to their natural home at the end of the day. There were still ancient elms to be climbed, and bigger kids to run away from.

I owned a real Webley starting pistol I'd got from some illicit swap or other. I can't remember whether my parents knew. It was treasured, lovingly taken apart, cleaned and polished. I even developed a callous on my finger through pulling the trigger that was designed for bigger hands than mine. Me and a group I was with were held-up and robbed by a bigger, more powerful gang than ours. My starting pistol went the way of all good things. Matchstick Island - land of excitement - land of fear - land of adventure. I guess I was about eight or nine then.

I started getting pocket money, the not very princely sum of sixpence a week. I didn't just get it. It had to be earned. My sister and I were allotted washing up to do. We used to argue about who would wash and who dry. There were odd shopping errands to be run and dad's bike to be cleaned. It was at about this time that I began to 'borrow' my sister's scooter. There was nothing I enjoyed more than rolling down the slope of the railway bridge on the way to the shops. More than once, to my mother's annoyance, I forgot the potatoes or washing powder as I pushed the scooter uphill several times for the sheer pleasure of rolling down at speed. This whetted my appetite for a bike. Oh what I wouldn't have done for a proper bike!

In the top class of the junior school, I had a revelation. It didn't come from heaven but in the form of a pair of spectacles. Those little round wire ones with brown plastic covering the wire and flexible springs to hook over the ears, much like Harry Potter's.

Thank goodness for the National Health Service. They were the most comfortable glasses I've ever had and they were free. I suppose the other kids 'took the Mick' a bit. I didn't care. I could read the numbers of the buses and people didn't look at me as though I was an idiot because I had to ask. A new world was revealed.

Some time before, my teacher, who I liked, had arranged for my sister to come from her class to read to ours. She was a precocious reader and there was a great hoo haa at home because she wasn't officially old enough to use the adult library but wanted to read books from there, rather than those designated 'children's'. My parents went to great trouble to see that she was given a ticket for the adult library. My progress as a reader was regarded as slow. I don't know the reasoning behind bringing my sister to read to our class. I think the idea might have been to spur me on but there was the implication that I wasn't as bright as her. I don't remember feeling resentment. I simply wasn't that interested in reading.

I wanted to be in the garden, watching ants as I tormented the poor creatures poking at their nests to see them scuttle madly about rescuing their treasured eggs; finding earwigs in hollow stalks of dried out, dead, delphiniums to wonder at their courage and strength as they nipped my fingers with the tiny pincers on their tails; watching grasshoppers and finding a chrysalis or balls of unbelievably fine thread forming a cocoon around hundreds of tiny spiders' eggs that, if prodded at the right moment, might send dozens of tiny white babies scattering in all directions. I liked to see the way caterpillars munched plants and the way certain caterpillars matched particular plants so that they were camouflaged when at home. More than once I was late for school through watching purple-black velvety caterpillars that looked for all the world like bits of stick until they wriggled sinuously to munch the leaves of privet hedges planted by the council as garden boundaries.

I remember the first time I saw a caterpillar crap. It was rich, dark green (the crap). I was astounded. Shit was supposed to be brown. Soil was brown and crap must have made lots of soil, it had to go somewhere and with all those people doing it every day there must be loads of it, though how did the sand and those stones get there? I'd have been about ten then. Mud was fascinating in its own right and even more so if you washed out bits of shell and different coloured sand.

I think my interest was encouraged because my short sightedness enabled me to see things normally sighted people could not. My eyes magnified things, so if I looked closely, that is, I put my face six inches from the object I was watching, I could see clearly. Sometimes I associated smells with things too, because I would get close enough to smell what was going on. Privet smells sweet in the spring, then as it flowers it smells of dog pee, and after the flowers are gone the leaves get tough with a distinctive bitter smell. I had an interest others could not understand. Added to that, I couldn't see the blackboard at school without glasses until someone realised I'd needed them.

Christmas came. I'd asked for a microscope, and that's what I got. It was cheap plastic and I don't think it really worked. I could only hide my disappointment. I'd expected to find the answers to mysteries that none of my family knew existed. I'd hoped for an extension to my wonderful glasses that changed my world. I didn't realise that to get the best from this toy, that may have worked, it was necessary to understand at least a little about depths of fields and how lenses worked. Had I been shown how to use the thing I might have got more from it.

At school we had nothing as sophisticated as microscopes, and lenses were explained by diagrams that bore little resemblance to my reality that amounted to bits of broken glass marble being used to set things alight by concentrating the rays of the sun. To describe these objects in terms so inexpressive as to amount to little more than a soporific drone diminished their fascination. What sad missed chances there have been due to poor education failing to use the natural curiosity that is so much a part of every child's makeup. A combination of things may have slowed my learning to read, though there may have been ways in which this was advantageous. I learnt to think and come to conclusions for myself. "What you lose on the swings you gain on the roundabouts," as Mum would say.

I liked to draw and paint and do things with wood, plasticine and metal. This too may have curtailed my reading. I wasn't just interested in painting pictures, I was interested in finishes. I made models and painted them; part of the challenge was to produce a good finish. None of my family shared these interests and in some ways they devalued them: my models, that were important to me, were either dusted or 'put away' and often broken in the process as a precursor to being thrown away as rubbish. Mum called the models dust harbourers. She didn't really want them around. This filled me with frustration and anger. I was becoming more adult and wanting space of my own. The overcrowding that my parents had suffered now began to come into perspective.

16

Paper-Rounds and Telly

Our house consisted of two bedrooms, a bathroom, kitchen, dining room and sitting room. It was a good house, clean, functional and dry but it wasn't big enough. The two downstairs rooms were separated by double doors and could be amalgamated by opening the doors to make one big room. When I was about ten it was agreed that my sisters and I should be separated. A *Put-U-Up* bed settee was purchased and this became my bed. Each evening the double doors were closed, my bed was made, and I went to sleep. This arrangement worked quite well from my point of view. I had the biggest bed ever and it was comfortable. The noise from the room next door didn't bother me.

All this changed with television. My father always promised we would have a television when the independent station came on the air. He lived up to his promise. I was delighted. I still remember looking forward to Friday nights. They were bath and 'Dragnet' nights when I could sit swathed in warm towels, drinking cocoa and watching the telly before bed. Thinking about it now, I recognise the programme as banal twaddle, but at the time I was innocent and thought it exciting stuff. *Quatermass in the Pit* was on Mondays and I had a special dispensation to stay up. That was one of the few horror movies I ever enjoyed. As time went on I began to grow disenchanted with the telly and quite often decided I would rather read.

When I was around thirteen I was allowed to do a paper round in order to supplement my pocket money. I think I'd started smoking by then and needed more money to buy tobacco. By that time the lovely big bed settee had gone, to be replaced by a second hand folding thing in a cupboard. It was so saggy as to be little better than a hammock. I get backache now at the very mention of foldaway beds.

I didn't take long to establish my place at the paper shop, and was soon marking the papers for other boys, as well as doing extra rounds when boys didn't turn up. I was beginning to earn real money. My father was a foreman in the London Docks and earned around twenty pounds a week. Some weeks I could earn two pounds ten shillings. That's two pounds fifty in new money. I could buy a packet of five Weights cigarettes for a shilling, the equivalent of five pence. There was a problem in that to earn that amount of money I had to be up at around five thirty in the morning, before the rest of the family.

I liked the job. Getting out when everything was quiet, when all was dark and eerie, was exciting. There was a businesslike feeling to the shop that made me feel I had a place in the world. The hustle and bustle as the papers arrived, to be tossed from the van in big bundles tied with sisal string, for Seeny the manager and me to carry into the shop. I can still hear the satisfying 'pop' as the string was cut, releasing the smell of fresh newsprint and ink as we broke up the piles to sort them into order, ready to be made up into the 'rounds' on the early morning erected benches. There was something tactile about the whole business that I enjoyed, as well as the busy comings and goings that I felt at home with. There were always small adventures, and I saw curious goings-on that fascinated me - policemen getting cups of tea and free cigarettes at our shop, and an odd nod, nod, wink, wink bonhomie between them and the manager I didn't understand that had a mysterious meaning I had yet to fathom.

On one of the rounds was a woman who frequently appeared in the flimsiest of nightdresses that showed her nipples, even in midwinter. Perhaps even more in midwinter. We weren't even supposed to say nipple in those days, even 'knickers' was a bit chancy. I was agog. She wore lots of make-up and pungent perfume, and used to lie in wait to open the door and offer me tea and a 'warm' and ask me to 'ring her bell' as she looked at me with a sideways slant and a lip curled smile. She scared me stiff, though at the same time offering forbidden possibilities and taboo temptation.

Windy weather made things even more exciting, more eerie than ever. In ominous gusts, shadows danced, billboards creaked and banged. Cats howled and the unknown lurked in every patch of darkness. Blue electrical sparks from the railway lit the sky, making reality flicker like one of Mum's old films. It was better than *Quatermass*, frightening, exhilarating, and real.

All this came as an introduction to the adult world, where things were important, feeding my curiosity with ever more tantalising mysteries. I had to be early to bed to be able to function effectively next day, but on the other side of the door, more than once a week, my sleep would be interrupted first by the dreaded theme tune and then *Dr Kildare*. I might not have been critical of *Dragnet* and 'The names have been changed to protect the innocent.' But *Kildare* made me sick, the simpering twerp. I had to lie in my horrible little bed, dragged out of its despised box each evening, and listen to that tripe. We had rows as I interrupted to yell sarcastic remarks about the trashy plots and poor quality of this inane nonsense through double doors, little better than sheets of paper as a noise barrier. A two-bed-roomed

44

house simply wasn't big enough. I had no space of my own. The garden shed or the inside of my head were the only places where I had any privacy.

ℰℰℰℰ

17

Secondary School

I failed the Eleven Plus exam and moved on to the Secondary School. Now I was pigeon holed and classified 'thick'. What was worse, I started to believe it. I was particularly unlucky because I was a part of what was called, the 'Bulge'. This was a way of describing the mini population explosion that took place with the return of normality at the end of the war. As a result a smaller percentage of kids passed the exam than during other years because the number of places stayed the same. In Dagenham we had the lowest pass rate in the country (There were less grammar schools than elsewhere). Had I lived ten miles away, I would at least have been a candidate for a 'Technical School'. In the event, I was destined for Bifrons Secondary Modern. My previous school had been well organised and fulfilled its function well. My first day at Bifrons was measured in terms of survival. New starters were herded into a corner and quite literally jumped upon by the older kids, who threw themselves into the herded crowd. Playtime was anticipated with dread because the older kids traditionally chased beginners with a view to forcing their heads into toilet bowls prior to flushing. I was lucky and got away with a ducking in a drinking water fountain. The official uniform was largely disregarded in favour of the tightest jeans possible, bootlace ties and hobnailed boots, 'all the better to kick with'. Fights in the playground were commonplace and the cry of 'Bundle' signalled a rush, with yells and jeers by all and sundry, to the source of the call. Generally, I, like most of the teachers, tried to stay away from brawls that sometimes resulted in quite serious

45

injuries.

I managed to talk my parents into buying me a pair of slip-on shoes with thick leather soles, to which I added steel tips. They were a match for hobnailed boots and made for better speed. I sat, and passed, the thirteen plus exam but by that time I felt the die was cast and didn't want to move again. I'd made some friends and moving would have meant Park Modern School. That would have been better than Bifrons but not much. I'd come to terms with the fight culture of the school by then. With hindsight I should have moved. "If ifs and ands were pots and pans there'd be no need for tinkers," Mum would say.

The only real fight I had was when a bigger youth tried to take my tobacco. He began with threats, but when I resisted he began pushing me around while I steadily retreated. We finished up on an untidy patch of ground planted with battered ornamental shrubs, fifty yards from the school gates. He sat astride my chest, whilst using my ears as handles to bang my head on the ground. In the long moment of crisis when everything slows, and lucid thought accelerates, I lay on my back, desperately searching with both hands for something to hit him with, fate presented a saviour, a hand-sized stone. He was lucky because if nothing else had presented itself, my thumbs would have searched out his eyes. I swung with wild desperation and all the force I could muster. He collapsed onto me, a great inanimate dead weight. All around us, kids were pressing in shouting and yelling, egging us on. Wriggling from beneath his inert body in near panic, then barging in a tearful rush through the gathered mob, I ran home. My arrival shocked my mother. I was spattered with blood. She took me to the kitchen to clean me up and assess the damage and asked, "What happened?" Still trembling, I replied, "I got in a fight,"   not mentioning tobacco. She ran water and took off my shirt. Washed clean, my bruised ears aching, then slowly relaxing to find other bruised and tender spots, it became clear the blood was not mine. "So what happened?" she repeated. "He had me on the ground and was holding my ears and bashing my head on the ground, and I hit him with a stone."

"Oh," was the only response.

When my father came home and Mum recounted the events of the afternoon, I was questioned but as soon as Dad knew my assailant was older and bigger than me, he simply said, "Well done son, don't worry about it." If there had been any trouble, he'd have backed me to the hilt. He knew the other lad was bigger than me and that was all the information he needed. He'd have supported me one hundred percent. Back at school the next day, there was an inquest. It transpired I had inflicted a wound that required several stitches, and he'd suffered concussion, but he was bigger and older than me, and not around to complain, so the whole event was forgotten. My reputation as a fighter not to be pushed around grew, and attempts to bully me declined, though when they happened, they were more threatening than before, having more to do with 'cocks and walks' than just being left in the peace that was all I wanted.

I developed a systematic response to attacks. I was the top spitter in my class. I could spit further than anyone. Spitting may be unpleasant, but so were my attackers. I'd spit in their faces as a dis-traction, then kick, aiming for the kneecap with a heavy shoe before running. I used this technique more than once. I even began to think of it as a kind of choreography: spit, balance, kick, balance, pirouette, balance, run. Our school was a place of learning. If you didn't learn to fight, life was misery.

Lenny Goosefoot had lived with the misery of bullying for years. (His name was a disadvantage without his being dim-witted). He finally developed a method of dealing with a bully when he bent down, grabbed his unsuspecting tormentor by the ankles and stood, tipping the brute backwards. This response was so shockingly effective it cracked the skull of the youth, so recently enjoying his vicious fun at the expense of poor Lenny, who, for merely defending himself after years of torment, was sent to an institution. That was justice in Dagenham and Bifrons in those days. There but for fortune went I. Since then I've always been wary of 'Justice.'

My troubled school career didn't improve. Workmen had been asphalting the roof of an old air raid shelter to waterproof it for use as a night-class motorbike workshop. They left large-headed nails scattered in a corner of the playground where we surreptitiously smoked. Our hideaway was on the route to the woodwork teacher's favourite parking spot. While we puffed away, keeping an eye out for teachers, we smirked and chattered about the likelihood of cars getting punctured tyres while we stood nails on their heads with the toes of our shoes. We talked of flat tyres as a huge practical joke. In the event the woodwork teacher managed to collect seven punctures: no joke.

We were soon discovered as the culprits and there was no denying, we had done the deed. We were told the police would be called. The truth was that the contractors had not been properly supervised and after weeks of negotiation and indecision about what should be done, it was agreed with our parents that the damage would be paid for by us out of pocket money. In the end, when all the culprits had made their contributions, it didn't really amount to a great deal. This taught me a lesson I've never forgotten. Think through the consequences before acting, another of Mum's clichés. 'Look before you leap.'

In the early stages when all this was going on I worried. My stomach felt hollow and my bladder constantly full. After three days real upset I convinced myself that however much I worried the outcome would be the same. From that day on, whenever I've felt myself starting to worry, I've always sung to myself:

'Why worry? Why worry?
Cos' worry gets you nowhere at all.'

I don't add the corollary: 'Do something constructive if at all possible,' because that's understood. If I sing this often enough it helps, even if it doesn't overcome the problem.

The whole sad business was a mess, not least because the teacher felt that we had some grudge against him, when the real problem was that we were just silly boys who hadn't considered the true consequences of our actions. Whilst perpetrating the crime I'd simply been thinking in terms of images and how funny it would be to see the tyres deflate, as if reality was a cartoon film. The truth was that out of all the teachers the woodwork man was one of my favourites. This episode turned into one of the most important and toughest learning experiences of my life. Relationships were soured and a whole lot of trouble caused by just a few minutes of thoughtless stupidity. What a sad lesson.

✥✥✥✥

18

Pigeons, Pets and Perverts

I went back to look at my old school not long ago. We expect things not to change but, predictably, the old place has gone, to be replaced by two and three storey, what we used to call maisonettes. I think that name has taken on a meaning that is strictly downmarket, so now estate agents describe these houses with something pretentious like 'city living town houses' rather than the local 'rabbit hutches'.

I had nothing against the school building. Like the houses around, it wasn't fancy, but it was utilitarian. I thought it was good. In summer the windows opened, concertina style, making the classrooms with their low sills almost part of the ever tempting outside. In winter the industrial scale boiler chimney belched smoke and great, solid, cast iron, radiators filled the rooms with stuffy heat, never matched at home. It's a shame the building wasn't the school. The head mistress's nickname was Droopy Drawers, and with good reason. As she lugged her heavy body up the steps onto the stage for morning assemblies, the bottoms of her knee length frilly drawers could be glimpsed. Even the teachers were embarrassed for her. She may have been clever but she was also a fool. One morning she mounted the stage to announce "In the last year this school had the worst record, apart from one other, in all London for court appearances of pupils." Our response was as resounding a cheer as I

49

ever heard. She was from a different world to us, with no idea about keeping discipline in school in a 'rough area.'

Her intentions were good but we regarded her as a joke. She was a poser. She always signed her name in green ink to appear distinctive. The only way she'd really have been distinctive was as a straight-man to a comedian, even then people would have laughed at her, not with her. She got the job during the war when the bottom of the barrel of teachers must have been clearly in view.

My friend Roy kept pigeons. Roy was a 'character'. His perception of the world differed from other people's. He was as funny as anyone I've ever met. His father worked as a chef in one of the big London hotels, and was eccentric. Their cooker was the exact opposite to ours; it was never cleaned. His mother did none of the cooking. The cooker was in Roy's Dad's territory and he had some quirky idea about it being left alone. Its top was black with decades of burned-on splashes from long-gone minor cooking accidents. Their house was an end of terrace. We would enter through a side gate and then through the back door into the kitchen, which, apart from the cooker, was clean but odd. The most striking oddity was the two handed saw hanging on the inside of the back door. It was almost as long as the door was tall. Each time someone entered or left, the saw swung and clattered, springing against the door to diminishing noise as it settled. The ark of its swing was worn into the paint. It had hung there for years. It was as if Roy and his family were unaware of its presence, though the rattling would have driven me crazy.

Roy's pigeons were really important to him, and his parents understood. In our home we weren't allowed pets. "Too much trouble," Mum would say, till eventually she relented when my sister begged for a budgie. It was a real concession because we certainly weren't going to have the cat or dog my sister craved.

Mum would glare at the cage saying "Look at the mess it's made." We were only allowed to keep it because we did look after it and because Mum grew fond of it. It even learned its name. It was called Picky. It could pick an apple to pieces in a morning and flick the bits all over the place and then say "Who's a pretty boy then." We laughed when it laid an egg.

Roy had dozens of pigeons with a whole shed to themselves. My parents would never have accepted that. One morning Roy asked me to carry a bird to school as part of its training. Near the gate Droopy Drawers saw us carrying the birds and made a great fuss saying, "Oh they're so beautiful, do bring them to my study," which we duly did. She bent to pet one. It promptly shat. Roy indignantly said. "Now look what you've done; you've scared it out of him" and marched out, genuinely affronted. I followed. Thoroughly annoyed and upset, he said to me, "If it doesn't get home I'll blame her. She scared the shit out of him, just looking at him." I released my bird with tears in my eyes. I could hardly walk for laughing.

Twenty thousand teachers were used to bolster the war effort and our school was blessed with some of the dregs of what were left - it was a shambles. 'Sid' Wills who ostensibly taught English and German, was academically more than well qualified, with a degree from Oxford. He'd taught at Manchester Grammar. The exact reasons for his arrival in Dagenham are unclear, but we can surmise. He had problems. Most men smoked in those days. I'd even heard of doctors recommending smoking to exercise the lungs. Sid was a slave to tobacco, even by the standards of the day. He would rather go without trousers than cigarettes. He'd have looked unnatural without a filter tip stuck to his lip. He smoked incessantly. His bedding must have been asbestos. Had it been cotton, he'd surely have created his own pyre. He would sit at his desk during lessons in an annex classroom, cigarette drooping from his lip, whilst Peter Stuyvesant's shares rose and ash quietly cascaded down his grubby old Oxford tie. The folds of his navy woollen blazer lapels were polished through constant hand brushing, whilst the fabric of his coat absorbed more ash, and smoke added to the kippered stain at the front of his receding grey hair. When I think of Sid I'm reminded of a Spanish Civil War poster depicting the degenerative effects of drink and cigarettes. His skin looked so dry and yellowed that I thought it should crackle like creased wrapping paper.

He didn't just stink on the outside. Inside his head was foul too. He had a penchant for sexually assaulting girls. He imagined he was charming when he said 'Du bist ein schone madchen' (You are a beautiful girl). He had more faith in this illusion than Icarus had in his wings. How he maintained it beats me, but he never gave up. He simply couldn't resist the temptation to squeeze a buxom young breast. He used to lean over a girl's shoulder as though pointing to something on the page of her textbook and enjoy a swift fumble. The whole class was delighted when Catherine Carver, who could pass for twenty, caught him a slashing stroke across the cheek with the edge of her ruler, causing a livid welt that lasted for days. That slowed him up a bit, but he still groped the quieter girls.

In German lessons a favourite trick with boys was to ask a pupil a question in German, to which the unfortunate would have no clue as to the answer, and then deliver a sharp whack on the head with his knuckles saying, 'Du bist ein dumkopf.' These words formed the core of our knowledge of German. In the last year he did it once too often to a big lad aptly named Broad, who became one of the biggest second hand car dealers (in both senses) in the East End. Broad retaliated, sending his desk flying, as he thrust himself upright, then drawing back, oblivious to his surroundings, as he balanced to lay Sid out with a stupendous straight right. I'm not clear about what followed but I have a feeling Sid never returned. I couldn't have been more pleased. I've never forgotten the bastard caning me in an English lesson for reading *Lorna Doone* when I was supposed to be doing clause analysis (By that time I had taken to reading as though books were water in the desert). Sid was as nasty a sadistic pervert as I've ever met.

19

Ben Er, 'Hit Me Keith' & Provence

Ben Er taught maths and physics. He wasn't a rat like Sid. He didn't smoke, but his skin was a close match for Sid's. He was the most phenomenally boring teacher you could not hope to meet. His face was so wrinkly it might have been ploughed. He was in his fifties, with thinning grey hair and crooked brown teeth that caused him to lisp slightly. He earned his nickname through his constant 'erring'. 'I want you to, er er turn to, er page six in, er your, em, er text books,' would be a fairly representative sentence of Ben's. He was quite capable of an er every ten seconds. Despite his dreadful delivery, he was one of the few who could maintain discipline. He achieved it through his dour, humourless personality and the soporific effect of his constant erring, backed up with a cane. His lessons were as entertaining as half an hour in a cold bath.

Not all the teachers were bad. The metalwork teacher was one of the reasons I didn't leave when I passed the thirteen-plus, but he left. A man called Mr Hames who'd been in the navy during the war replaced him. He'd enjoyed his war. He treated us in a way that he appeared to think was fair. God knows where his ideas came from but he split John Smith's hand with a cane weighted with a leather strap bound on with electrical tape, turning it into a whippy long-handled cosh. I had the impression that he probably thought flogging was a good idea. If the 'cane' hit your fingers, the resultant swelling might stop you writing for a couple of days and leave a rash of tiny blood blisters that lasted for weeks. On this occasion the end of the weapon landed at the base of John's thumb splitting the skin sufficiently to require two stitches at the local clinic. Something must have happened after that, because subsequently the tape and leather disappeared. I don't remember what his teaching was like so I suppose it was adequate. During lunchtimes he sometimes taught boxing. A big lad who later had a trial for the Wasps rugby team got into the ring with him and when Mr Hames said, "Hit me, Keith, go on, hit me," Keith did as he was bid and promptly laid him out. We had to give him credit: when he came to, shaking his head to clear the starry haze, he said "Well done, Keith, that was a good punch. You well and truly caught me there." Not long after that the lunchtime boxing lessons ceased. Mr Hames had realised he wasn't as tough as his dreams led him to believe. I want to know what he did in the navy.

The history teacher, Mr Bowen, was distinguished by a scar that ran from his eyebrow and down his cheek to his mouth that it was rumoured he'd collected from a sword slash during the First World War. He did his best, but thirteen year olds from Dagenham don't find the foreign policies of King Charles 1 very interesting, even when the story's spiced with the scandal that the king enjoyed the company of men more than women, so Mr Bowen faced an uphill struggle. When he took morning assemblies he'd get us singing to raise the roof and sometimes we'd have an audience in the street, our singing was so rousing. He should have been the head. He had our best interests at heart and understood that there was a need to build some community spirit in the school.

It was Mr Bowen who organised the school trip to Provence, in the South of France, although we were supposed to be learning German. Our parents scraped together the cash to send us and it was worth it. It was the experience of a lifetime. No flying for the likes of us in those days. We went by train. When we got to France the seats on the trains there were made with wooden slats and there was a toilet at either end of the carriages. It was just a bowl with a four inch pipe attached through which the railway sleepers could be seen whizzing past. There was no flush. People gravitated to the centres of the carriages because the stink near the toilets was so horrible. By the end of the eighteen-hour journey we'd discovered that the most comfortable place was in the luggage racks. We arrived in vivid bright sunlight that made colours sharper and brought Van Gogh to life for me. We saw little water mills that floated on boats alongside the banks of the Rhone. We saw the Pont du Gard aqueduct; the bridge at

Avignon that inspired the song; and the amphitheatre at Nimes. The striking thing about the school we stayed in was the smell, a mixture of rank French cigarettes and garlic; it was so light, with geckos basking in the sun on whitewashed walls. We ate pigs' brain and it was okay, just different. We were even allowed to drink watered raw red wine like no wine we'd tasted at home, and joked with French fishermen on the Mediterranean coast, despite not being able to communicate through language. The experience was one that I wouldn't have missed. I never ever thanked Mr Bowen, but I've felt indebted to him ever since for such a wonderful time in an unaccustomed country with glorious hot sun.

Back in Dagenham other teachers came and went with great regularity. At one time we had four Mr Jones. That made life really difficult at times, causing farcical situations that we pupils set out to engineer as often as possible. None of the Joneses lasted very long. They were probably a product of the government trick of extra grammar schools in Wales, where in some places the pass rate for the eleven plus was as high as thirty percent. Quite a contrast to Dagenham's three. I wonder if this wasn't a government ploy to carry off the cream of the crop in the Welsh Valleys, sometimes known as Little Moscow, in an attempt to control left militancy in the area.

20

Disrespect, Locks and Keys

I did quite well at school but the school was so poor that to be good there was to be at best mediocre elsewhere. Mum and Dad let me get on with it. I don't think they were delighted at my progress but there was little they could do to help. I was more interested in painting and drawing than the other subjects, perhaps due to the way the other subjects were taught. I'd taken the role of class clown-cum-weirdo. The other kids respected me for being a bit crazy. I used to say "Thank you" when I got the cane. It hurt like hell but it got through to the teachers better than anything else I could think of. I was being bloody minded and 'cutting off my nose to spite my face' according to Dad, though I think he understood it. I was showing the family stubbornness he inherited from his father. It was the best way I could express my contempt for their unreasonable violence. There were those not just trying to maintain discipline. A couple were just plain vicious whilst one, I think, got a sexual buzz, his flushed face lighting up with a kind of demonic glee, as he wielded his cane.

I might have been mischievous like Mum's Dad, but I wasn't 'bad'. You could argue I had an evil sense of humour but it was humour, after all. Putting empty quart beer bottles outside the head-mistress' office or wrapping a dog turd in newspaper soaked with a drop of lighter fuel, then lighting it at the vital moment as the silly old bat with predictable respectability set about stamping out the fire, still strikes me as funny. Look at it from my point of view. In general, I thought the teachers were crap and saying thank you when I got the cane was my way of saying 'up yours'. They understood that. Generally my attitude didn't make me popular with the staff; we shared a mutual disrespect.

In metalwork lessons, my best friend Allie and I made a model car with a real back axle, drive shaft, and springs, as well as double wishbone independent front suspension. The body we carved from blocks of balsa wood glued together to accommodate the working parts. It was a scale model of a single-seater Coventry Climax, formula one racer, with a five c.c. glow plug engine. It went like a rocket. We ran it attached to a control line guidance system. It was excellent. This got us a special dispensation to use the metalwork room and all the equipment. People didn't bother so much with health and safety in those days, and sometimes the teacher wasn't around to supervise. He was a great bloke, but like anyone with half a brain, he was making his escape and leaving. I didn't blame him. If it had been me, I'd have been out of there as if it was setting my trousers on fire.

At the end of a science lesson Ben had left his keys on the edge of his bench. We'd been watching them throughout the lesson. There would never be a better opportunity. Allie and I had discussed getting hold of a skeleton key and taking an imprint so that we could copy it. This was our chance.

"Go on. Go on. There's nothing he's gonna do even if he thinks you're daft or something. All you've got to do is get him to write something on the board. He won't be able to believe you're really taking an interest. Tell him you want to make a speed controller for an electric model car you've read about in one of the modelling magazines. Ask him if a Wheatstones bridge would do it. You've got to do it now. Look where his keys are. We'll never get a better chance. Get him 'erring' and there'll be no stopping him. Go on."

"All right, all right, but hurry up. I hate the smell of this place and old Ben stinks of it. He smells like the undertakers behind the Co-op and I'll have to look at his horrible crooked teeth, and I'll want to laugh. He'll know something's going on if I start pissing myself."

The bell rang. We nervously hung back as the rest of the class stuffed exercise books into bags amid the clatter and scrape of tall wobbly lab' chairs before pushing and shoving their way towards the crush at the door. Allie was brilliant. I didn't listen to what he said. I was busy watching, waiting my chance. Now was my moment quick, quick. Quiet.. all four eyes needed. Which one? Which one? Careful, quiet. Got it, quick, matchbox open. Squash. Got it. Done. Hwooo... Ha ha. Just like in the *Great Escape,* old Ben was a hopeless goon. Looking cool now the impression's in the plasticine, I nudged Allie in the back. Ben was well away,

"It's not that simple you know. You'll need to er count the coils on the armature er er er, you'll em have to be careful too that you er don't crack the er varnish and er er that would cause a short through the coil and er then er well it wouldn't emm be a coil would it? If you're really serious about this I er had better er see the magazine. These things aren't as simple as you might think. Ehm Anyway you'd better get to

57

your next lesson now. If you're really serious about this you'd better er come and see me er at er er lunch time but er not today."

Imagine how an hour and a half of erring, ahing and uhming encouraged us to look longingly at the door and the playing field. Our main pastime during his lessons was taking bets on how many ers he'd manage in a minute. I don't know if he realised that his nickname was Ben Er. If he did you'd have thought he'd at least have attempted to do something about it.

***

"Yes sir we've got some things to do to the car. We crashed it when we ran it in the playground last night and the radiator and two of the wishbones are bent," I lied, and promptly went to the metalwork room to make the key that I used to create havoc in the rest of the school. It was a small victory but a victory nevertheless. They may have scored ten points to my one but it showed I was still alive and not crushed by boredom nor ready to become factory or cannon fodder yet.

I had fun with that key. I locked teachers out. I locked them in. I got into the caretaker's cubbyhole and made tea on his gas ring during wet playtimes. Once I even got into the staff-room toilet after school to plant a banger on top of the cistern with a time fuse (just a piece of cotton string dipped in salt-petre) that I could light from outside with a dog-end through a skylight. That helped one of the idle gits to do his job in a hurry. Okay I was an out and out pain in the backside to the teachers, (especially the one caught by that banger) but from my point of view they should have made more effort to make the lessons interesting. They were plain lazy and churned out the same old stuff year after year, like robots. With a bit more willingness to see our point of view we'd have been more interested and we'd all have had a more fun, teachers included.

21

There's a New World Somewhere

As my school days neared their end, my prospects, although bleak, looked better than most of my schoolmates. The economic outlook was rosy. Enoch Powell was making controversial speeches about immigrants and immigration, in direct conflict with government policy encouraging immigration to keep inflation down. There were plenty of jobs and wages were on the up. With Rab Butler's Education Act of 1944 providing free education till fifteen for all, the government had accepted training and education as valuable and, even at our school, where academic achievement came about, despite, rather than because of the school, we were encouraged to take GCE exams. I thought I had a fighting chance in about four. I'm not aware of the details but the school received extra cash for each exam entrant. I had been entered for about half a dozen subjects. That meant I was due to stay on until I was sixteen. As part of our introduction to the world of work we were taken to different local factories where staff were needed.

One particularly sticks in my mind. It was a bath enamelling plant. The operation was carried out by heating of the cast iron body of the bath to dull red and then carefully sprinkling a coating powder from something like an oversized pepper pot. The resultant smoke and chemical stink was admitted to be poisonous by the people giving us the tour and they told us it was a good idea not to stay at the job for more than about six weeks, longer than that and permanent damage to health might ensue, but the money was good. We were taken to other places where opportunities were available - Cape Asbestos and a tap and valve factory where the fumes were not much different to the bath enamellers. Such were the opportunities available to the pupils of Bifrons Secondary Modern. I wonder why our 'careers' teachers took us to these hellholes?

***

My sister brought home a man who had been her boss while she was temping at an advertising agency. I can't recall his face but he was quite a character arriving at our house in a sports car. It was probably a heap of junk. He took the door off to get out. I thought that was really quirky, James Bond, super cool. When he came in, I was drawing in a big sketchpad and 'just like that' he offered me a job working at his agency in Soho with time off at college to do graphic art. This offer set my eyes sparkling. Not considering the grim trip each day crammed in the 'tube' but thinking of the glamour, David Bailey, Michael Cain, and other famous names all revolving around Soho, the swinging sixties come to Dagenham. I didn't have a clear picture in my mind of what it truly meant but sensed it was a once in a lifetime opportunity.

I had been to the National Gallery and enjoyed the feeling of being at the centre of things, even though I was ignorant and had no real understanding of what I was looking at. I'd been to the Tate Gallery to hear David Hockney lecture and was impressed when he answered my diffident question. "What makes fine art fine art?" I remember his answer now. "Fine art contributes something new that changes the world around us." Brilliant, straight 'off the cuff'. It changed my attitude to art. Previously I had cynically thought the whole business was steeped in bullshit, especially the modern stuff, though the trip to Provence had opened my eyes to Van Gogh. Those few words made it clear he'd really thought about the question. To think I was being offered a job that would get me close to that world, where people 'made a difference,' away from the rows of rubber stamp houses that made Dagenham the epitome of dead end conformity.

My eldest sister had gone to teacher training college. I believe the result had in some way disappointed my parents and it had cost. I was regarded as less bright, so sending me to college, even part time, may have been regarded as a poor investment. My mother's response to the job offer snuffed out my small spark of hope. "Lots of people can draw. You should get a proper job." I wasn't quite fifteen at the time and didn't have much say. The offer wasn't taken up.

It was odd that my sister's boyfriends seemed to be harbingers of jobs for me. The place I actually got was an apprenticeship at the Ford Motor Co. Mick, my sister's latest beau, worked there and he recommended it as a good apprenticeship. I don't think he had anything against me, he was genuinely happy there. The places at Fords were sought after and the Company went to great trouble to select what they thought were good prospects. I don't remember exactly how it came about that I applied, though I remember doing a series of weird tests set by the Institute of Industrial Psychology.

They had us passing a metal ring attached to a rod over a length of bent wire while we wore earphones that shrieked if the ring touched the wire. They also hooked us up to something that looked like a computer disk the size of an old twelve inch vinyl record, with a magnetic stylus that we were supposed to hold as near the revolving, highly reflective, like-pole magnetic disk as possible without touching it, while still attached to the shrieking earphones. How this was supposed to give them information about me as a potential employee beats me, though it did look impressive. It wasn't long before their aptitude tests were proved to be less than one hundred percent. I very soon hated the way the company worked and they soon formed a pretty negative opinion of me. Looking back, I was never suited to working in a big factory, I was too interested in the world around me. From the day I started, I was a square peg in their regimented set of round holes.

There were medicals to be gone through and multiple-choice questionnaires at unaccustomed, intimidating venues. I had taken the tests with the approval of the school. It became clear later they either didn't expect me to pass or didn't consider the consequences, because in order to be included in an induction block of apprentices I had to leave school mid-term. When this happened there was a great fuss and the school demanded I take the 'O' levels I had been entered for. Eventually it was arranged with Fords that I would be allowed back to school to take the exams. In the event I was placed behind the invigilator, on the stage, in the school hall, at the table where the headmistress sat for assemblies. This may have been intended to intimidate. If that was the case it was a total failure. It placed me in a position where I could pull faces at the back of the invigilator and mess around with imaginary frilly drawers. It didn't matter to me whether I passed or failed. I'd got my job. Putting me on the stage put some of the others doing the exams at a disadvantage because I was able to act the fool and distract their attention.

Having left school nearly three months before the exams, I was quite smug when I passed in three subjects with virtually no effort at all, a performance better than the average for those who stayed for the full term. This makes me sound conceited, I probably am. It helps if you went to Bifrons Secondary Modern in Dagenham. When I left, Droopy Drawers' only comment in my school report read "David is good with his hands." I didn't know what 'damning by faint praise' meant then.

22

Work, & Face to Face with Ugly

The day I started work I was overawed by the sheer size of the factory. Thirty thousand were employed, if all the shifts were included. They told us with pride there were seventeen miles of road, a gas works that was on the national grid and the same with the power station. There was a jetty with capacity for three ships of up to twelve thousand tons each, and a blast furnace and foundry as big as anything elsewhere in the country. It was the biggest factory of its kind in Europe. I've no idea how we were introduced to the 'Trade School' where we were to work. From the main gate to the apprentice school was about a mile, three quarters of which was a good-sized road that led to the bus station, cycle sheds and car parks. Then we walked a quarter of a mile to the security point, where there would be several security men to control the flow through turnstiles and walkways. Yellow, steel tube railings separated about eight paths, each a yard wide set-up, much like the entrance to a giant football stadium. Everything had the look and smell of greasy coke. If it was wet, puddles carried a film of oil that reflected light with a rainbow sheen. Apart from that and grimy yellow painted handrails everything appeared desultory grey. Battered Fordson tractors dragged steel plates around over the slippery, black greased tarmac. They didn't use trailers. I suppose the plates were easy to load.

A hundred yards from the security point a road ran between the factory buildings. Each day I walked through the dark chasm created by buildings tall enough to block the sun, except when it was overhead at midday. If there was no sun it was overpoweringly depressing. No living thing had any place there. Concrete walls extended upwards ten feet, above were dirty steel framed windows, each with hundreds of twelve by ten-inch panes. It was ugly, massive and ugly. Walking that sterile road each day, my stomach knotted at the gritty, bleak deadness of it all.

23

A Little Fun

We started in basic training where for three months we were taught the rudiments of mechanical engineering, first of bench work, essentially hack-sawing and filing accurately, then we moved on to lathes and turning. As we learnt the practical side of things theory was taught to match, so we learned how to measure with a micrometer and vernier. The work was quite interesting and there were times when something funny happened, as when one of the less bright youths was asked how many thous' are there are in an inch? The answer came, "Oh there must be thousands of the little bastards."

***

Seventeen shillings and sixpence I was paid and money was stopped from that to pay for tools and the white coats they made us wear as apprentices. We were supposed to be grateful for the opportunity to work for them, as though we were in the middle ages when apprentices went and lived at the house of their employer. I continued with the paper round when I first started working, to make my money up to something half reasonable, but it was impossible to carry on and I had to take a drastic drop in income. Social life on ten shillings a week was almost impossible. I could just manage the occasional Friday night trip to 'Billy Walker's Roller Skating Rink' at Forest Gate.

That was fun. There were girls but what girls, some of them were madder than us boys. The evening would start reasonably sedately with loud music on a tinny PA system. There would be waltzes and old fashioned classics, things like *The Hall of The Mountain King* designed to give the less proficient skaters a chance, then the music would gradually speed up so that to be other than a reasonable skater would be to cause a nuisance to the swirling throng. Next came the announcement to clear the floor for the ladies exhibition and a few girls in tutus would pirouette, and glide gracefully on one leg, forwards, backwards, spinning, enjoying their moment of glory. They were quite good as far as it went but there was no proper training so the whole thing was fairly pedestrian. Many, girls as well as boys, thought they were prissy and snobbish. They had to have more money than most of us to buy tutus so it may have been partly envy. Then there was a break, a short intermission for drinks.

After that the real action started. There were good skaters employed for peanuts, as marshals, whose job it was to trip those going too fast. Now the competition began. The crowd circled steadily faster while the marshals wove in and out, trying to trip the

64

fastest. The faint hearted crashed or left the floor as the business of staying on your feet grew increasingly difficult. Some of the best skaters were girls and they'd continue in the thick of the melee often taunting the marshals who were trying to trip them. Just as things were turning to pure mayhem, the music stopped and the floor was cleared for the highlight of the evening - the boys' race. It was mad. There simply wasn't room for the number on the floor skating flat out. Crashes were inevitable. There were injuries, cuts and grazes, but the element of danger was part of the exhilaration and fun. There were occasional broken arms and other more serious injuries but surprisingly few given the 'Hell for leather' pace. There was seldom a real winner. That wasn't the point. The whole time was a celebration of bubbling energy and youth just at the threshold of adult life.

Skating ended, everyone gasping for soft drinks. We rode home on a bus filled with noisy chatter, rounding the evening off with girls taunting the boys into ever more silly showing off, all of us filthy from the dusty rink. Great times!

24

Inspiration, Passion & Considered Brutality

Basic training finished, we moved into the main area of the 'trade school'. There were over a thousand apprentices and not one girl. There were four women working in the offices. Two of them were young. Good for the young women; not so good for us apprentices. It skewed the atmosphere of the place in an ugly fashion, creating an institutional feel.

The main workshop was divided into areas where we learnt each discipline of practical mechanical engineering: turning, milling, grinding, welding, sheet metal, machine repair and fitting. By mastering all these elements, theoretically, a person could make any part for any machine. We weren't expected to become masters of all the areas, but we were expected to gain a good grounding in the whole lot. We spent six weeks following a set path of exercises in each section. It was a good practical foundation in engineering, there can be no doubt, and has served me well. To understand any trade well is useful. Not only does it enable you to do that particular work, it teaches patience and tenacity, enduring assets.

James Brindley, the famous canal engineer, began life as a wheelright. He made his first wheel completely wrong. Wooden wagon wheels were dish shaped. This gave them their strength. Brindley got the dish the wrong way round, making the wheel weak and useless. His employer nearly sacked him. Like the rest of us, great men learn by their mistakes. Mindset is half the battle; determination is as important as talent. Einstein, when asked "What makes a genius?" is said to have replied "Ten percent inspiration and ninety percent perspiration."

To work hard and well at anything other than brutal hard labour it's necessary to enjoy the work. Really good quality work demands passion. I enjoyed handwork. I'd been to the Tower of London and seen guns that went back to the sixteenth century. The mechanisms fascinated me. I'd been employed to become an engraver. I'd seen a pair of beautifully engraved Purdy shotguns that had inspired my choice. This, I thought, would have an artistic content that I would enjoy - it might even grow to be a passion. I felt this need even then.

Soon after I started, the question was repeated. "What area do you want to specialise in?" I reasserted my commitment to engraving, only to be told. "Oh, engraving, that's a dying trade. We're not teaching that any more." This was a dispiriting blow. I didn't want to stand in front of a machine all day, every day, simply working to measurements and drawings. I wanted something more creative. My despondency showed. Bullies pick on the weak. I was young and vulnerable. Life was drudgery.

The philosophy there could be said to fit a Social Darwinist pattern. 'If you can't take the pace, don't join the race': or 'When the going gets tough, the tough get going,' were the sort of the phrases they used. Bullying was part of everyday life. Toughen up or be proved a loser. I became a target. I'm not big and I was a misfit. A square peg. A common practice among the bullies was to creep quietly either side of their victim, quickly grab the tails of their white dustcoat and pull, ripping the coat's back seam. If an instructor saw you wearing a ripped coat you would be taken to task and told to get it repaired or get a new one. The cost of a replacement was three pounds, more than three weeks' wages. Two apprentices gave my coat this treatment. They didn't know I'd gone to school at Bifrons. My despair burst into anger. The bigger of the two was called Wheelan. He had fair hair and the beginnings of a double chin. He was my age, but already his head blended into his shoulders. He had a neck but I'd have been hard put to say where it began or ended. He was three or four inches taller than me and more heavily built; fighting him would have been foolish, I'd almost certainly have taken a beating and apart from that, fighting was a sacking offence. Something had to be done if my life wasn't to be unendurable.

I roughly tacked together the torn seam and made knuckle-dusters to keep in my patch pockets. They'd help even the odds with the weight difference if the need arose. Then began the watching; anger fed my determination. He threatened but it was through nervousness. Steadily I watched. He pushed me around whilst I egged him on with expressions of scorn as the fingers of at least one hand slipped home into my solid, confidence boosting, match levellers. His bullying demeanour evaporated into edginess as I taunted him. I had him worried. Still I continued, quietly staring, now close, now from a distance, steady, following every move for days. My tenacity paid off. A couple of times he called me names, threatened and pushed me around telling me to 'fuck off'. His nerve was failing. I regarded him with distainful looks and continued quietly staring. He was rattled.

My chance came. At tea breaks he spent his time at a particular spot near the back door to the trade school, loud-mouthing and smoking with his cronies. I took to sitting on a tall pile of pallets behind the door. He was aware of me and occasionally glanced edgily my way. Beside me I kept balanced a length of timber. My time came. He'd momentarily forgotten my presence, his back to me and I above him. Quietly I lifted the baulk, pointing one end at his neck. Aim. Thump. I knew exactly where to hit him, I'd learnt that boxing. Not too hard. I didn't want to kill him. He went down.

His mates and other apprentices crowded round, none sure what happened as, dropping the wood, I slipped down from the pallets and unbuttoned his coat. Fear helped me focus on my one objective, his coat. Both he and his cronies were too stunned by my wildness to do anything as I wrenched it off him, close to ripping it more than once as I pulled and tugged, scrambling with terror determined to peel it from his lumpish body. He wasn't out cold, just very dazed. That made it more frightening, but helped - he wasn't a dead weight. I threw my ripped coat into his lap and slipped his on with a look of distaste. Feigning calm, looking contemptuously at my stunned audience I strolled quietly back into the workshop as the bell rang to call us back to work. When I left, Wheelan remained slumped against the pallets, whilst some of the apprentices tended him. I learnt later that the cleaner found him shortly after. I don't know what was said but I was called to an interview with 'Slippery Lips,' the personnel manager. As I passed Wheelan, his little, pig pink eyes were watery and his face whiter than usual as he whispered. "I'll get you, bastard," with no conviction at all. Elation… I laughed scornfully. I looked a clown in his coat three sizes too big, the hem six inches from the floor. He looked even sillier squeezed into mine gaping at the back. I managed to talk the laundry man into swapping Wheelan's for one that fitted me. I'd no idea what Wheelan did and I didn't care.

No one tried to bully me after that. Sometimes they called me Psycho. That was fine. There were times when I felt crazy in that dreary workshop. No one pushed it. Just the sight of him made me feel like whacking him again; they knew, so did Wheelan.

25

'Slippery Lips', Ford Canteen Belly and Probation

I stood before the desk. It was my first close encounter with 'Slippery Lips'. He didn't smell nasty. I can't remember his real name. Everyone called him either 'Slippery' or 'Slippery Lips'. He was shaped like a Buddha. He combed his long, thin, *Brylcreem* greasy, grey hair to cover his round balding head. His round belly matched his spherical head and his part inflated balloon cheeks. His face was a map of blood vessels, dense over his little pointed nose thinning towards the periphery where his skin might have been taken for putty. He seldom moved, seemingly moulded to his chair, legs spread to accommodate his blister belly. He was wearing a grey three piece suit flecked with reddish brown, colour co-ordinated with his face. His tongue worked continuously, determined to wet his pink pouty little mouth. His froggy eyes flicked around puffy sockets, as though on ball joints. Invariably the middle drawer of his desk, rumoured to be full of porno' magazines, lay open three or four inches, his lips wet due to constant lascivious excitement as his restless eyes slyly sought some sick picture.

"Have you been fighting?" The blotter on his desk absorbed a shower of spittle. I suppressed edgy laughter, feeling more giggly than if I'd had a couple of pints. "No." I couldn't suppress a smile. I nearly wet myself trying to look a picture of innocence.

"Where did you get that coat?"

"I think there was a mix up at the laundry." It was all I could do to stop bursting into paroxysms of laughter. He must have known.

69

"Hmm, go on. I don't want any more trouble from you."

That was it. I'd met a Company 'people' person. It wouldn't be the end of our acquaintance. I didn't care. I jigged to the toilet by the back door then out to the pallets. I wasn't nervous. I just thought it might be better if no one found the brass knuckles I'd left on the pile of pallets.

Life settled to a more or less dreary, rhythmic routine. I enjoyed some of the work, but operating the machines left me bored. Everything was done by numbers. I thought there must be a way of feeding the numbers into the machines automatically. There seemed little point to doing such mundane tasks by hand.

Twenty years later I was gratified to note that with computers this pointless drudgery was eliminated in favour of computer programming. Welding I enjoyed because it involved a more intuitive skill; and "fitting", or carrying out the final finishing work and putting the parts of a machine together to work properly I found enjoyable and challenging too.

I grew friendly with a lad called Tim Trevallyan. We and a couple of others formed an informal defensive group to combat the Wheelan crowd. Tim came from Cornwall. He and his mother lived in a pokey old flat near my grandmother's at Silvertown. I didn't ask where his father was and he didn't volunteer information. Tim's mother doted on him and despite their rotten accommodation, she'd contributed towards buying him a smart new motor bike, even though she hated him riding it.

For some reason we couldn't meet during work time. We needed to discuss details of a trip to a bike race at Brands Hatch. We arranged to meet in the canteen where neither of us usually went. It was so awful. We both bought cream doughnuts. They were sweet, if just marginally palatable. We made our arrangements, but on the day neither of us was fit to go. The cream in the doughnuts was infected with salmonella. We were among seventy off work with food poisoning caused by infected Chinese dried milk in the cream in the doughnuts. Two went to hospital and nearly died. I came out in plum coloured scaly blotches. The doctor said, "Oh, you're lucky it's come out through your skin." I told him, "If this is your idea of luck, you can keep it." Back at work I saw Tim in passing.

"I want to talk. Meet you by the clock at lunchtime," he said," I went. He stood waiting holding a brown paper bag.

"Were you late this morning?" he asked. There'd been a snarl-up at the gate that morning and many had been late.

"I came on the push-bike so the traffic didn't bother me much, and I just made it."

"I was," said Tim as he drew a cream doughnut from the bag.

"Four minutes. They're going to dock my wages. Stand in front of the clock for a minute," he said as he stuffed the doughnut into the mouth of the clock, forcing it right in with a foot rule, "but I'll get it back tomorrow, when the clock's got food poisoning."

I had another 'run in' with Slippery when I was caught reading. A tabloid was acceptable, so I'd hidden my book in a newspaper, laid it on the tool cabinet by the machine, and was quietly reading, while keeping a weather eye on the machine as it laboriously brump, brump, brumped its three quarters of an hour, indefatigable way through a two foot long piece of steel. To do the job that way was silly from a real engineering point of view, a bit like painting a barn door with a half-inch brush. It was a waste of time, just a way of drawing out the time spent on the section to fill the six weeks allocated.

The instructor caught me reading not the newspaper but a book and worse it was *The Ragged Trousered Philanthropists*. I had no idea at the time but this was almost as bad as spitting in the boss's face.

"How do you like working these machines?" he asked. He was very approachable, merry even. He had a casual style and I took him at face value.

"Do you want an honest answer?" I asked.

"Of course."

"Well I don't mind working the machine too much but I hate the stink of cutting oil, (They called it *suds* and advised keeping hands away from it as much as possible because it caused dermatitis) and I

71

feel as though I need a bath before I go home, and with a cut like this that takes three quarters of an hour, I get bored stupid."

"Oh, you do?"

And with that he casually strolled away, not even telling me to put the book away. I thought nothing more of the incident until the end of my time on the section. When I received my report from that section, it read, "David shows no interest in engineering whatsoever." That was it. I was dumbfounded. I'd done the work, gained reasonable marks for the jobs I'd done. What was going on? It wasn't till much later that I realised that the instructor couldn't have been more insulted if I'd raised two fingers and told him to 'Fuck off'. I believe he felt I was treating him with utter disrespect, and now I can see that in a way I was. If I told the truth I couldn't think of a less rewarding way of spending my life than working a milling machine; I'd rather have swept the streets. I'm not sure why, though it's partly to do with the way milling machines work, there's ugliness and inelegance about it that you have to feel to explain. There's something tooth grindingly unsexy about milling machines. That's the best way I can express it. Of all engineering machine tools mills are the least sensual.

***

Another message from Slippery: "Report to my office in the morning." I knocked. His eyes flicked towards the glass door where I stood, though his head hardly moved. His tongue made a couple of circuits to guarantee wet lips before he called, "Come in." He looked the same but now a cloying, sweaty smell pervaded his office. I made an effort not to screw up my face as I asked,

"I had a message you wanted to see me?"

"Yes. It's about this report from Mr Butler. He seems to think you're not interested in the work and he tells me you've a tendency to be rude."

I was astonished. I'd still not associated the incident with the book with all this. To this day I'm not sure, but it's the only thing that I can think of to link to the report. I was too surprised to say anything. Slippery asked "Do you want to say anything?" Still at a loss, I said "No," though in my mind I was still wondering what was going on. "Hmm, well, you seem to have a bad attitude and leave me little option but to put you on probation." He sprayed. He usually sprayed pronouncing 'tion.' His tongue was too big for his tight, puckered, little mouth.

"I expect your performance to improve. Over the next three months I'll be watching you carefully. Your timekeeping is nothing exceptional; there's room for improvement. I don't want to see you again for three months. If I do, you'll be on your way to the main gate. Understand. Go on."

My marks for the work I was doing were better than average so this whole business came as 'a bolt out of the blue'. On the machine repair section I did quite well and this fitted in with working on real cars. Most of the apprentices were interested in cars and engines and there was great competition to work on cars rather than machine tools. There had been some question as to whether or not I might go to Le Mans with the GT40 because I'd got on well with the instructor when I'd done some experimental work on the suspension. It was glued with epoxy instead of bolted. This was regarded as a privilege. Needless to say a period on probation meant withdrawal of any privileges. In the event I was sent to work on setting up at a less than glamorous agricultural show at Earls Court. As we put the thing together, (hard work because it was heavy, designed to carry three tractors) two other apprentices acting the fool accidentally drove a tractor into a wall almost punching a hole through into the street beyond. They weren't put on probation.

26

Clean Noses, Beds of Roses, Sunshine, Tonsils and Sport

"I don't mind the work so much, Dad but the people who run it are just horrible. The odd one's all right, but even the good ones you can't trust. They seem to pick out the creepy blokes specially. It just makes it a rotten place to work." All he said was, "Life's not a bed of roses, you just have to learn to 'keep your nose clean' and put up with it. You're young and we all kick against the traces a bit but you've just got to learn that you're only cutting off your nose to spite your face if you keep it up." Of all the things in my life the only decision I truly regret is staying at Fords, then. I should have left and done something I wanted to.

***

I must have got under Butler's skin much more than I realised at the time. Later in the year, at the depressing time shortly before Christmas when the days were short and we were arriving and leaving work in cold darkness, I watched a last shaft of sunlight that against all odds had made its way into the building for a minute or two before sunset. If I'd been religious it would have been an act of worship. Butler stood beside me asking, conversationally "What are you doing?"

"I was just watching the last of the sun shining through that patch of window." I was both shocked and sad at his response.

"Get on with your fucking work. What do you think this is, fuckin' Butlins?"

The Company encouraged sport, and the football team did well in one of the top amateur leagues. They encouraged and helped talented individuals, expecting in return that those people represented the company. Not unreasonable. I was extremely fit through riding my bike hell for leather to work to 'beat the clock.' The company held a sports day and I just lost the mile to another lad who ran for Ilford Harriers. I was surprised because we both broke the company record and I knew that I was better at longer distances. I had a problem though in that as soon as I really tried I knew I'd get tonsillitis.

Mr Mc Namara, the assistant manager of the trade school, was a great sportsman, five foot ten, looking five foot six, he was so wide. His game was rugby. When I came second in the mile at the company sports day he approached me to run for the company. I told him I couldn't do it because as soon as I started to train seriously I'd get tonsillitis. I'm sure he didn't believe me and talked to me twice more, implying that to not represent the company with such talent was to show lack of commitment, and in some way was a slight to the firm. That annoyed me. I went there to do an apprenticeship, not to carry their flag in sporting events. If I ran for anyone it wouldn't be Ford Motor Co. I did run once or twice for Essex Beagles but it was no good, my tonsils were too rotten.

Later on when I was twenty-eight my tonsils were so bad that I went to work one Saturday morning and by lunchtime they were literally green. I could stand up just long enough to cross the road and phone the doctor. He was at a party on the other side of town, somewhere near a private hospital. Standing made me dizzy, with spots before my eyes. I wasn't too bad sitting but not really fit to drive. I got there, at the end of my tether and managed to walk into a private hospital nearby, where the matron said "We can't treat every Tom, Dick and Harry who walks in here with a cough or cold." I let myself go and passed out. I woke on a couch with the doctor leaning over me.

The matron said. "Where's your wife?"

"I haven't got a wife."

"Huh you need a good woman."

Despite feeling awful, I couldn't miss the opportunity for such a wonderful line and told her laughing and hurting all at once.

"Lady, the last thing I need at the moment is a good woman."

"Huh she grunted," looking daggers,

I nearly died laughing at the sight of her face. I laughed so much I wasn't sure if I felt better or worse. The doctor told me. "Take four of these a day." They were half an inch long black and red penicillin capsules. He arranged an operation to take my tonsils out. Three weeks later, they were gone. I never looked back. If only they'd taken them twenty years previously. They didn't remove tonsils in Dagenham, apart from in exceptional cases. They argued it was a bad policy medically - not mentioning that it cost money.

27

Happy Campers, Girls & Burning Rubber

The rest of the first year passed uneventfully. I passed the exams; few failed. The holiday came. I spent it with my parents. It was the last time I went on holiday with them. We went on a coach. I expect it was cheaper than the train. The journey took twice as long as might have been expected as we sweated through traffic jams on roads built for horses and carts, all the way to a holiday camp at Weston-Super-Mare.

Windy Weston on the Mud, it was terrible. I spent most of my time feeling embarrassed. Happy campers: Oh dear, oh dear. The food was poor, the entertainment was generally bloody awful, with tawdry smut and dreary innuendo passing for humour. I'm not sure that the 'chalets' were built as barracks during the war, but that's what they were used for, and it showed. They were little more than garden sheds painted on the inside. The only place to be was in the swimming pool, though to stay in for more than ten minutes was to court a bout of pneumonia.

With the second year of my apprenticeship, the wages increased significantly and I'd grown used to 'keeping my head down' in the 'Trade School.' I bothered no one and no one bothered me.

I had some cash now and could think of a social life. Girls were becoming important. I went to the local Palais a few times with some other apprentices. Some people called it the 'Meat Market'. Girls stood along one side of the hall and boys on the other, all dismally failing to look casual. I danced with a few and tried to talk but either they or I had so little in common that it was painful. The whole business was so forced and tense as to be uncomfortable, even embarrassing.

I did enjoy it just once when I met a couple of girls who were there simply to have fun and mess around not determined to look smart or cool or on the hunt for a husband. They worked for a big tyre firm and had come in a small lorry with several large tyres in the back. Instead of being all tarted up, they were dressed in jeans, not the done thing in those days. If they'd been males, they wouldn't have been allowed in. I enjoyed myself and I think they did. I've wondered since, if they were lesbians who'd not quite come to terms with their sexuality. Were we three misfits together? I didn't see them again because they came from miles away and were seeking a wild night out. As it turned out, it wasn't really wild at all just good fun. I didn't feel the need to drink to relax, simply chatting and acting the fool, while on other evenings drink was a necessity to make the time bearable.

As apprentices we began to fit into the ethos of the factory. I sometimes used to get a lift from one of the other apprentices, whose parents were better off financially than most, and had a car. There was a fault in his interior light and we decided the company could afford to replace it. Our wages were paid by the government through a scheme to provide training, so even then we felt we were being exploited when we were clearly doing work for the Company, while being paid by the government. We ordered a set of drawings that showed the interior light, then went into the factory where the cars were being assembled and asked around the men working on the line where we might find the interior light we wanted. We learned they were issued one at a time as required. We were wondering what to do when a foreman asked what was going on. We bluffed that a redesign of the interior light was being considered and we were checking some details.

"Oh I'll stop the line for you," he said obligingly. Unscheduled stoppages of the line had caused strikes and could cause the Company to lose thousands of pounds. As soon as the foreman turned his back we made off at a run.

On another occasion that same youth decided he would like to fit a better carburettor to his car. At the time a Weber 40 DCOE carburettor would have been the envy of every car-owning apprentice in the factory and we decided to reroute one over the boundary fence, to collect later. We filched the carburettor and made our way to the place chosen at the boundary fence, but were seen by a security man. The swag was dropped in haste, as we ran the shortest escape route, across a pond where molten slag from the blast furnace was poured to cool, prior to being broken up for road-stone. It was not until we were several yards onto the glassy smooth surface that we realised it was still hot, but we continued, frightened out of our wits, as we smelt the rubber of our boots burning on the hot slag. As we neared the centre, the pond turned from dull grey to dull red. It was still so hot that I could feel the soles of my boots melting and becoming liquid and slippery as I ran. I can't ever remember being more frightened as I willed the surface not to crack and wished myself weightless in a miasma of burning rubber. We escaped, but I never attempted anything like that again.

28

Art, Swagger & A Chinese Meal

I joined the local art club. The members were mainly middle aged or older and pleasant enough, but hardly consumed by creative fire. There was a club 'Professional' who'd sold some paintings and had a facile knack, proficiently producing a reliable product. He worked to a formula. He'd have been ideal decorating pottery. He was quick and insisted that a limited pallet lent discipline to the work of beginners.

I had no training; I was there to sample something outside Fords that could provide me with an unknown something I felt was missing. I turned out some dreadful rubbish, and knew it. I earned some cash posing for a life class but I only did it on the understanding I could wear swimming trunks. I did it for an evening class and didn't feel comfortable. There were some odd characters sketching me. It was an interesting experience though, different and oddly upsetting. I couldn't put my finger on why, it was bloody knackering physically too.

The club ran an outing to Bishops Stortford. Off I went with easel, oils and a piece of hardboard about two foot square, found laying around in the garden shed. I painted an Essex barn, a traditional higgledy-piggledy, tarred shiplap thing with lots of texture. It wasn't the worst thing I'd done. It was about average for the club - bloody awful - but it provided me with an introduction to two girls from the local teacher training college. By the end of the day I wasn't interested in painting; my thoughts were elsewhere. We packed up and I went with the rest of the club to a Chinese restaurant. I couldn't afford a meal so I sat in the back yard under an awning by the toilets. It was drizzling. To pass the time I made a pastel drawing of a row of dustbins standing on wet black bricks that shimmered under a stuttering yellow light as the spatter of rain broke its continuity. It was casually done on brown wrapping paper, just something to hand. The result was the best thing I'd ever done.   Someone coming from the restaurant looked at my drawing and asked,

"Do you want to sell that?" I was stunned.

"Well yes, er, yes."

"How about a fiver?"

Not believing my luck and hesitantly saying, "That'd be great," I carried away a fiver and he carried away my drawing. I walked into the restaurant, sat down and ordered a meal.

"Where did you get the money?" someone asked.

"Oh I just sold a drawing," I coolly replied, swaggering a bit but can you blame me. What a fantastic day.

I took one of the girls out the next week. I thought we got on quite well and she was great to look at but we didn't have much in common and she lived too far away. The evening wasn't a failure, but nothing came of it. It was a pleasant interlude.

29

Physics, Riots and Castrol 'R'

As apprentices, most of us couldn't afford cars, but motorbikes were a real possibility. To be without a motor bike was to be an outcast. Motorised transport was a must. I bought a lowly old *Sun Wasp* fitted with a 98 c.c. Villiers two-stroke engine. It had no rear suspension, just springs at the back of the saddle and 'girder' front forks. It was cheap, a real bargain, and I soon discovered why. It went perfectly well for about half a mile and then slowly coughed and spluttered to an ignominious standstill. I pushed for a while and then tried starting it again, and again it sprang into life. Half a mile later, putter, sputter, and it died again. This sequence of events continued until I reached home, thoroughly dejected. I had no one to help so I had to figure out the source of the problem myself. Off came the cylinder head and all appeared to be well. I could not afford a new gasket, and having learnt a little, I used a blowlamp to anneal (soften) the copper that made up the outer casing of the old one. With the head back on, kick and away we went, only to stop after about half a mile. What was the matter with the damned thing? I was beginning to think like an engineer.

Physics said that the engine should work. Experience showed it worked, so there was a cause; something was wrong, but what? I knew I had to check all the elements that might cause it to stop when it warmed up. This I knew was called analytical thinking. I'd checked the spark, time and again, and tried more than one new spark plug. The spark was fine; it had to be something else. There were two other elements that were essential for the engine to work: first the presence of fuel; second, the satisfactory compression of the vaporised fuel. Off came the head again. There was clearly fuel aplenty. The piston was wet with unburnt petrol. This time, seeing the gasket so compressed, I decided to try to do something to return it to a more nearly new condition. I took it apart to discover a telltale track across the inner packing of asbestos. I'd discovered the source of the problem. As the cylinder head heated up, the gap between it and the cylinder expanded and allowed gas to begin to escape through the more lightly compressed gasket, reducing compression so the engine stopped. I did what I should have done in the first place and replaced the gasket to make my little motorbike a runner. It was by no means glamorous, but it went. Now I could ride to work without the physical effort of a pushbike.

I soon learnt there were disadvantages. One was money. To run even this rather sad little bike cost. Insurance, petrol, tax - it all added up and ate into my meagre wage at an alarming rate. Added to that was the cold. Motorbike clothing in those days consisted of ex-army or air force equipment sold off cheaply at Army Surplus Stores. As far as it went it was good value but on a dark frosty morning the cold crept through my clothes and into my bones with a viciousness

I'd never known before. I reverted to riding my push bike. I'd realised I actually enjoyed it, relishing the awareness of my body doing what it was made to do - move as fast as possible, flushed and warm rather than sitting frozen rigid, teeth locked against the all-pervasive cold.

I still wanted to leave Fords, and spoke to my father yet again about it. Again he advised patience. By then I was making a real contribution for my keep. "Wait till you're out in the factory, it'll be better then." I waited and managed to get through the second year more or less uneventfully. Summer came and I'd saved enough money to swop my unfashionable little Sun Wasp for something more exotic. I bought a Bianchi Tonale. The name on its own was enough to give it glamour. It was a 200 c.c. four-stroke capable of about eighty five miles per hour. It had a fancy shaped petrol tank with slick paintwork, a chain driven overhead camshaft, aluminium racing style wheel rims, really big brake drums and a well designed frame. It had style.

I rode it a bit and, pushing my luck too hard, came off. I was lucky I suffered nothing more than grazes. I went with friends to Brands Hatch and Snetterton but the races didn't really interest me. Motorcycle race-goers are mainly of two types. There are those who genuinely go to see the excitement of the race and there are the ghoulish, who without admitting it, hope to see the blood and gore of accidents. I wasn't really interested in the racing; I went for the engineering. For me the machines were an art form.

My lovely Bianchi spent most of its time in pieces. I polished the con-rod and inside the crankcase. I fitted a bigger carburettor and valves. I Stellite welded the cams, increasing the lift, and made varying shapes and lengths of exhausts. As each of these jobs was finished I had to test the result. Allie from school had another fancy, though relatively small bike and we bought a stop watch to check the effects of the various modifications we made to our machines. We used to go to the straight road alongside Barking Power Station on a Sunday, when it was deserted, and roar up and down, timing different runs. I finally achieved close to a hundred miles an hour.

It was the summer of the riots at Brighton and Clacton. Allie and I and one or two others went, not to fight or riot but simply to get away from the dreariness of our lives working in the factories of London's East End. As I saw it, the 'riots' weren't really riots at all. I was a Mod on a motor-bike. There was little real fighting but there were mobs that the police felt threatened by. We just regarded the whole business as a bit of fun. Had we come from Eaton or Rugby then I have no doubt that the National Dailies would have put the whole thing down to youthful exuberance. As it was, we came from the East End and the papers must have been short of real news, so they branded us rioters. The police were determined we were a threat and hounded us for simply riding around in groups. The world was changing. The young were becoming a section of society in their own right, recognised as a separate group, distinguished by a set of values and aspirations different from their parents.

By the end of the summer I'd come off the motorbike several times. I've still got the scars to prove it. Thinking back I was so lucky. Each evening as we left work fifty or a hundred motor bikes of all sorts and sizes, ridden by apprentices, filled with glee at having got to the end of another day at the factory, lined up at the exit of the car park while a traffic policeman blocked our path in favour of buses. We sat astride our machines, revving the engines waiting for the copper's arm to drop and him to scamper away as we slipped our clutches to leap towards him. Then the race was on to the traffic lights at the other side of the railway bridge as we roared, hearts in mouths, jockeying for position, regardless of anything but the melee around us, the smoke and 'Castrol R' fumes. I still find the smell of 'Castrol R' exciting. All the racing bikes used it. It was a vegetable based, particularly light oil and wherever there were race enthusiasts there was sure to be the tantalising aroma of 'Castrol R'.

While I was at the trade school several apprentices were killed riding motorbikes. I sometimes rode pillion with Allan Leader, an old school friend. Thank heavens I wasn't with him when he rode through the gap between two cars to find a girl who judged she'd have time before the cars were upon her, crossing the road directly in his path. His machine hit a tree some distance away and was found with the speedometer registering eighty-five mph. The girl was killed outright and he died several months after.

Tim, of the food poisoned clock, had one cheek of his backside ground away as he slid up the road, depleting the muscle on his buttock to the point where the medics fixed his hip joint so that he could only bend his leg at the knee. No more motorbikes for him. My friend Allie had his thigh broken in two places when a car hit him side on. When he came out of hospital he was scared half to death crossing the road. I went and saw a lad I'd been to races with called Alec who was in hospital after he'd smashed into a traffic sign on a roundabout. His face was wrecked and an eye damaged. He'd been told that he could undergo several more operations to rebuild his face but he left the hospital to finish his racing 'kneeler'. Months later he was killed riding a motorbike and sidecar.

I rode my bike to Clacton with a girl riding pillion and on the way back came so close to the side of a lorry as I squeezed past to overtake that later I found green paint on my jacket. I have to admit to being a bit shaken myself. She was hysterical, tearful and hit me when I stopped. I found later she'd gripped me so hard she'd bruised my body through my fur-lined jacket. A week after that the engine blew up. I managed to replace the engine, then came off the bike for the thirteenth time and decided I'd tempted fate enough and sold it. I realised then that young men and fast vehicles are a fatal combination.

30

'Outward Bound' & Punch-clock Pain

Before leaving the Trade School all apprentices were sent on an 'Outward Bound' course. I was due you go in the winter of 1963. That was the second worst winter since the war. It snowed a couple of days after Christmas,, and the snow lay a foot deep not melting for six weeks. The crowd I was supposed to go with went to the Lake District and helped with mountain rescue. They dug out sheep from snow drifts, went skiing, and generally had a wonderful experience, even staying an extra two weeks helping the emergency services. I languished in bed with tonsillitis. I did go on the course later in the summer and had a wonderful time. It was the best thing that happened to me in all my time at Fords. We climbed Helvellyn and Skiddaw; rowed on Windermere and walked Striding Edge. I had the best holiday of my life and it went on for a whole month. I was eighteen then and weighed eight and a half stone when I went. I was fit, but built for distance running. When I came back I weighed nine stone and never lost the weight. What a highlight - great food, lots of exercise and even the odd dance at weekends where I met girls who didn't grunt and exchange stupid knowing looks.

We went to the cinema in Ambleside, so different from Dagenham or anything in London. It was tatty and small. We thought it odd and funny that the little elderly lady who sold the tickets then picked up a torch and guided people to their seats. At the interval the same lady sold the ice cream. Part way through the second half, the film broke to light humoured jeers and booing. Of course you'll have guessed who the projectionist was - none other than the lady who did everything else. She ran the place single-handed. She did it with good-natured willingness and a hint of humour that made her part of the show, and gave her dignity. We might have been in a foreign country. It rained a lot but the rain was soft and gentle, living dew, wonderful. A tantalising peek at what life could be, poking fun at the reality of Dagenham. According to the Duke of Edinburgh Outward Bound was 'good character building.' I had the time of my life. Did I have good character already?

The Outward Bound course signalled the end of my time in the Trade School. We were given a choice of departments where we were to begin our true working life. I chose pattern making, where models of castings were made prior to being sent to the foundry for production. Much of the work was in wood, with an artistic element that appealed to me. I was accepted but very soon learnt that the wood dust filling the air caused my nose to dry out, making the inside of my nostrils permanently sore and bloody. By the time it was concluded that my physiology made it impossible for me to work in the pattern shop, nearly all vacancies had been filled.

This meant another interview with Slippery Lips, a circumstance holding little promise for my future.

'Ah Misster Ray,' he sprayed. 'I only seem to see you when something goes wrong.' I resisted the temptation to say "That's your job, so it's not surprising." Pursing his lips in a prissy wet smile tucked deep between his fat cheeks, he seemed pleased to tell me "The only departments with vacancies left are 'Tool Trouble' in 'Crown Wheels and Pinions', and the Foundry or Blast Furnace. Most apprentices don't want to work in either the Foundry or the Furnace. They tend to be very dirty. I'd suggest Crown Wheels, the work there is more skilled, though I'll leave it to you." It didn't matter to me where I went; I was sick of the whole business. I guessed all the jobs were going to be awful.

"Well I'll try the Crownwheels then."

"You can't just chop and change to suit yourself as and when you fancy you know. I'll speak to the manager in Crownwheels. That'll do then."

I was dismissed. I spent another week with a sore nose and then they started me in Tool Trouble in Crownwheels and Pinions. There were two lines of machines in a factory building several

86

hundred yards long. One side of the building was dedicated to cutting teeth on crownwheels the bevelled drive gears for back axles. A matching set of machines on the opposite side of the building cut gear-teeth on pinions, the gears that drove the crownwheels in completed cars. The teeth were cut by six foot long cutters called broaches that in their turn had tungsten carbide teeth ranged along their length, at intervals of about half an inch. My job was to replace worn teeth. The work involved undoing an Allen screw, taking out the blunt tooth and selecting a sharp one from a hundred different sizes and kinds on the racks of my trolley, then making sure to carefully measure its depth setting, to match the measurement on a drawing. Each broach carried a hundred teeth or more and I was timed having to fit a target number of teeth each day. I earned seven pounds a week. The trolley I pushed, they told me proudly, was worth eighteen thousand pounds; fifty years wages. They should have understood that telling me was rubbing salt in a wound from my point of view.

All day long the whole building rumbled and shook with heavy background noise, overlaid with the constant dzzzippp, dzzzippp, as the broaches around me carried on their incessant work. A fortnight was enough. The prospect of this drudgery, with the foreman constantly leaning over my shoulder urging me to go faster, day in, day out, for the next three years, minimum, epitomised for me the most unendurable, tense, boredom, denied even the relief of heavy exercise to vent the pent up frustration and cancerous anger seething in my gut at my situation. Time to go... Time to get out... Out. Out. Out... Each minute I wanted to get up and run to escape the oppressive place.

The punch clock dominated my life. The days when the seasons ruled and time was measured by memories, myths of ancestors, moon and tides, dearth and plenty had been overtaken by Henry Ford's obsessive system. Time was manacled to a clock, whilst I was manacled to time, each minute measured, stamped and accounted in a ledger. Time no longer ticked quietly or peacefully by. Seconds were not accounted; only minutes mattered as punch clock digits clunked each passing. People no longer human - just numbers. Seasons - even day and night, indistinguishable, dominated by an interminable cacophony of black noise as machines pressed, drilled and ground out money in 'Ford Time'. Daylight was abandoned in favour of fluorescent tubes. Me - moulded, crushed, crippled and categorised to fit Fords monstrous ledger. T1052 clocked in, clocked out, clocked in, clocked out, another day nearer death and freedom.

At home I told my parents I couldn't carry on. I didn't feel suicidal. I felt angry. I just wanted to escape that destructive, mind numbing, straightjacket world. The very thought of the place made me feel like screaming the foulest language I could think of. It was no consolation that I was skilled. To think - Jesus - I was one of the lucky ones who might have some sort of prospects, a chance of escape from this life, enslaved to a system of mindless drudgery. Dad cautioned me, saying that it would be silly to waste two years of the apprenticeship.

"If it's so bad then go and see the personnel man again and ask for another move." I made another appointment with Slippery.

"I simply can't do this job," I said, "I'm just not cut out for it and if that's all there is I'll have to leave." Just one more word to push me, and it would have been with joy I uttered the words.

"Give me my cards." I'd have given six months wages to say those words.

"You can earn a third more on nights and there is always lots of overtime available in Crownwheels and Pinions. With a bit of overtime on nights you can easily earn double the money you'll earn on days." His face was bulging, contorted eyes squinting, and fat little lips stretched taut over his teeth. Perfect inspiration for a gargoyle. I'd not seen him give a smile, the full works, before.

I didn't need to ask why they were short of staff in 'Crownwheels and Pinions'. No one could stick the job. Soul destruction under pressure; no wonder there was plenty of overtime. They wanted to make me a wage slave.

"I can't do it. I just don't like the work. I like mending

machines but I can't stand doing the same thing over and over all day long, especially when it's so easy to make a mistake with someone constantly standing at my back badgering me to go faster."

His tongue slipped swiftly around his shiny fat little lips. "Well in that case all I can offer is the blast furnace." He smarmed, grinning, smug. The foundry and the furnace were to us as Siberia was to a Russian.

"I'll go there then."

ৡৡৡৡ

31

Blast Furnace Basics

That was how I came to work on the blast furnace. The odd thing was that it was the place that suited me best. Slippery wasn't lying when he said it was dirty. There was dust and grit on the ground and chemical filth in the air. In certain places they gave us plastic plaques with patches we were to watch. If the patch turned grey it was time to go because the gas was dense enough to kill, but at least there was space to move around and I could step outside and die under the sky. With over three miles of road and the plant spread over a wide area, there was no way to run the place other than to allow people autonomy. All the jobs were different, so time and motion wouldn't work either. I could cope with this, even if it was a filthy, smokey, depressing place to be. I wasn't to be imprisoned like some poor animal in a zoo, to be driven mad in a box and die of a broken heart or spirit. No creature deserves a fate like that. Better to put the beast out of its agony, clean dead.

I don't remember the first time I went there. All I have are impressions of smoke, galvanised chain link fencing, tar-coated corrugated iron, or concrete buildings, railway lines and asbestos and

89

asphalt lagged pipes. There were railway lines everywhere. Anything that wasn't grey or black was brown. Nooks and crannies were filled with drifts of grey coke dust. If there was any wind we walked around with eyes screwed up like Tuaregs in a sandstorm. At lunchtimes I became aware of it in my mouth as an accompaniment to my cheese, putting the sand in my sandwiches. What was worse, I didn't know until later, was carbon monoxide, everywhere, invisibly poisoning everything.

***

"Ah, Dave, you're the new apprentice."

"Yes."

"I'm Frank Rance." We shook hands.

"I'll be your foreman. You'll be training as a fitter. I'm going to start you in the main workshop while you get to know your way around. You're not very big and it's heavy work, so I hope you're fit… OK. Go to the stores. That's the window in the wall over there. Get some overalls and a toolkit. If anyone starts talking about skyhooks, air balls, or long weights, take no notice, they're acting the fool. Here's the order for your kit and some tool loan tags."

Looking back, it's as though I'm in the office in the middle of the workshop. The building is a fairly new standard factory structure with a big roller shutter door at one end. In effect it's divided into four quarters. The quarter where I'm standing is an open space with big silver painted stanchions at either side supporting a five-ton gantry crane. The floor is good smooth concrete. On the floor in the middle of the area is a grab from a crane. Closed, it would be fifteen feet high. At the moment it's laid open, the buckets are a bit taller than me. It's as big as our living room. Every so often it reverberates with a shattering rattle as a riveter closes another red-hot rivet in one of the lips. The noise is unbelievable. It's like a pneumatic road drill inside a big iron drum.

In the other corner is the biggest blacksmith's forge I've ever seen. Just the air pump that replaces the bellows is two feet high, with a big motor to drive it. There are two big anvils and a brake press. This too is big, fifteen feet long and really solid. Looking at the label two hundred tons/sq in" pressure. Wouldn't want to catch my finger in that.

Littering the floor like dead snakes, dusty, dirtied rubber pipes run to bottles of gas welding gear in sack barrow frames for mobility. A welder using an acetylene cutter creates great showers of sparks to the accompaniment of a satisfying hiss as he slices through rusty steel plate an inch thick. Everything is big and even though the roller door is open the place is full of the acrid smell of stick welding. Blue ark welding light flickers from behind screens, reflected by the walls, in concert with their crackle and spit, sounding like loud frying bacon. All this noise is obliterated when the teeth shaking clatter of the riveter's hammer suddenly rattles so loud as to clamp my jaw, skewering my ears with pain. At the stores two men are in front of me, one leaning forward on the shelf looking in towards the steel racks tidily laden with all kinds of things from light bulbs and rubber gloves to weird unidentifiable objects made from an assortment of materials. The other, turning back to face me, smiling, says.

"New are you? You're in for a treat here, son. Probably spend half your life hanging around here waiting while the buggers in there sit drinking tea all day." A voice from inside the stores retaliates,

"Don't take any notice of that idle git. Spends all 'is time 'ere causing trouble so he don't have to do any bloody work." The man at the shelf takes his order and looks at me, grinning, saying. "That's right son. You want to get in front of him. Spends his life looking for a long wait. He'll hold you up all day if he can."

It's dirty here but the atmosphere is like walking into a public bar after a spell in a penal colony - so awful was Crownwheels. There people smiled like hyenas, if they smiled at all; they spoke only when the job demanded, and there was constant tension. Happiness was an alien state. Here people are relaxed, talking normally rather than scurrying to keep pace with the machines. No one here forces you to put your hand up for a relief to take over while you go for a pee. Life carries on in a normal way. The man ahead of me says goodhumouredly.

"It's okay, son, take no notice of this lot. You can go in front of me if you want." - standing back to let me past. "And you, Wally, look after him. We can do with all the help we can get," he calls to the storeman who, taking one look at me, says "Overalls is it? Well we don't cater for flyweights, as a rule, so I s'pose you'll have to roll 'em up till we get you sorted out properly. I'll speak to the laundry bloke Friday so you won't get anything fits you properly till Friday week. That's the best I can do. And a tool kit's gonna' take time so you'll have to come back for that. Come back after dinner. I'll get you some loan tags sorted out as well, and you better bloody look after 'em too. I don't carry the can for anyone getting stuff nicked, or nickin' it either. Come back after dinner. I'll see to you then." Passing me a thick cotton boiler suit, saying "What's your name?"

"Dave Ray."

"What's your number Dave?"

"Tee, ten, fifty-two."

"Okay, Dave," writing the details in a pad. "Come back after dinner and I'll have your tags and kit sorted out then."

32

Last Chance or Madhouse

As I walked back across the workshop to the foreman's office I passed a welder, short, shorter than me, surreptitiously chalking on a canvas welding screen - Fuck off Brackett noisy bastard -. He whispered conspiratorially to me.

"Fuckin' noisy bastard's deaf as a post. Fuckin' racket don't bother him." The riveter was Brackett. I'd met Trevor. He was a 'character'. He was excused shorts in the army because he had the biggest penis I've ever seen and he wasn't shy about letting you know. At the slightest provocation Trevor would wave his member like the member for Park Lane might wave his Parliamentary papers at the threat of nationalization. He had five kids. I can't imagine what his wife was like but she has my pity. Not only did Trevor have a stupendous prick, he was nuts. Five feet five of utter madness, causing havoc wherever he went. Welders were set to replace worn crosses on checker plate as a safety measure when there was little else to do. Trevor didn't make crosses; he wrote Trevor. Everywhere you went, you walked on Trevor. He was like a mischievous ten-year-old with a taste for malicious practical jokes. We didn't need gremlins - we had Trevor. He dropped a poly' bag full of water sixty feet onto the head of a foremen, as a joke, and nearly killed him. When another man was leaning on a bench where there was a steel floor, Trevor crawled under the bench to weld the steel tip of his boot to the floor. The man attempted to move and almost broke a leg. Trevor lost us the right to phone home when we were going to work overtime because he phoned Canada for half an hour at a cost of £120. A man's wages at the time were twenty pounds a week. Trevor was an exhibitionist nut, but there were plenty of others who didn't wear their madness so lightly. The blast furnace was the last chance for misfits between normal society and jail or the madhouse. For the workforce it was jail and for management it was Warley, the local asylum, where Fords was said to have an option because twelve percent of management ended there.

Frank Rance led me into the fitting shop opposite the canteen. It was fifteen yards long by ten deep, separated from the main workshop by steel and wire mesh partitions. There were two big lathes that took up all one corner on the right hand side. The rest of the space on that side was filled by a shaping machine. On the left side of the shop was a huge bench fitted with six big vices. The benches in Fords were the best I've ever seen, solid, inch thick, cast iron. A small one weighed a ton. This one, laden with dirty bits of machinery, weighed more than double that.

On the wall between the bench and a big pillar drill in the corner was fitted a blackboard with a hook near the top. Below the hook was the unmistakable circular imprint of a dartboard. The lathe in the corner was operated by a swarthy man whose name I learnt later was Frank Vellucci, who'd never got over time spent fighting in Korea.

The machine nearest the door was run by a big, heavily set man with strong features, and deep set eyes under dark brows, and a thick mop of hair. He watched his machine, moodily taking three steps one way, then three steps back, up and down a wooden duckboard coated with hardened black muck and grease. Small shiny chips of swarf embedded here and there shone from the polishing soles of his restless boots. He walked as if pacing a prison cell, occasionally wildly yelling odd remarks. "Come on you boys. Get a bloody move on." Or "Two more minutes and you can drink some lovely canteen tea, boys." The tea was infamous, made with the cheapest tea leaves available and interminably stewed. If two foremen walked together it would be, "Noses to the grindstone you boys. Busdrivers." Foremen were called busdrivers because they wore white dustcoats with coloured collars, much like the holiday coachdrivers of the day. On a bad day it would be. "Come on you suck-arses, get polishing them noses." This was Tom Wyatt. He resembled a caged animal, with his constant pacing, giving the impression he hated his job. Surprisingly he was quite a pleasant person and, contrary to first expectations, he was more normal than many others working there. The yelling may have been a relief of boredom or perhaps a warning. As for the job, I could never understand whether he hated it or not. I do know that he was waiting to pull an elm dartboard from under the cupboard where it lived, soaked in a specially made round tin of rusty black water, to hang it

on its hook by the bench and practise or play, he didn't care; his darts
made his life endurable.

33

"Get on With it, You Lazy Bastards!"

The shaper - a kind of flat lathe with a reciprocating slide fitted with
a cutting tool, rhythmically cut thin slivers of steel. After each
forward cut, the tool moved back and the work-piece moved sideways
a small set amount, to bring the next sliver of metal to be removed in
line with the tool. Beside it sat a big man with light red-blond hair
turning white and a fabulous beer belly. Frank Rance introduced me.
"This is Gilley, he'll show you the ropes." Then he walked
away. Gilley introduced himself quietly and pleasantly, speaking with
soft rolling rs of Scotland. "And what brings you here? Been a
naughty boy have you? Don't worry too much. It's dirty, but it's better
than across the road there. We manage to manage them all right." He
nodded, relaxed, towards the office. I went through the tale of
engraving, pattern shop, and crownwheels, to my arrival at the blast
furnace, at pains to make clear I didn't think I'd been 'naughty'.
"Ay, well, you'll find life has its ways of pushing us in the
directions it wants, rather than the ones we want. It would na' do for
us all tay be rich and happy or we'd probably be less satisfied than we
are, and we'd have tay find something to fight about to make life
interesting" - all spoken with a gentle mocking half smile.
His machine stopped the tsss clunk, tsss clunk, it made while
working, indicating the end of its cut. He stood up slowly leaning to
switch it off with deliberate concentration. Turning and extending his
big hand he said,
"Ah'm Gilley. And you?"
"I'm Dave, Dave Ray."

"Well. Hello, Dave." He stepped towards the bench to introduce Jack. He was five foot eight or nine, with thinning, grey wavy hair and a genial, plump, reddish face - fiftyish, his middle spreading with age, not quite fit enough for this sort of work.

"He used tay work maintaining buses for London Transport so he does nae know much about engineering. Ay, and he's terrible slow," Gilley drawled with a chuckle.

Jack's rejoinder was pure East End. "Huh, take no notice of bloody Scotts bleeders; all they're good for is bleedin' shipbuilding. Precision to the nearest 'alf inch, and if 'ammer don't work, get a bigger 'ammer. Either that or riveting like that noisy bastard Brackett. What's your name? I 'ope you're not another bloody Scott. Ah'll be pickin' up a Glasgow accent and turning native deciding to support Celtic and 'an spittin' at the mention of Rangers an' eating flamin' porridge and totty scones if we get many more."

Wyatt yelled. "Get stuck in, you boys. You're not paid to stand gossiping all day." Both Gilley and Jack looked around to see a blue collar on a white coat (Different grades of foremen had different coloured collars and blue was the top before a suit) emerging from the hallway at the far end of the workshop. So Wyatt's shouting had a function beyond staving off boredom. He'd just issued a warning there was a foreman about. Later I realised Wyatt acted as the workshop lookout only half aware of what he was doing. He'd started a tradition. Anyone seeing a foreman slipping quietly into the shop might let out a yell." "Get on with it you lazy bastards," or "Get your arses in gear, you lot. It's not tea break yet." Then heads would turn, looking around, checking movement around the workshop. Sometimes there'd be a combined yell, especially if there were several foremen about, then the whole shop would take up the cry as someone, acting as conductor, shouted, "All together… Get on with it you lazy bastards." And two dozen voices would respond in unison. "Get on with it you lazy bastards." Disrespect for foremen oozed from the performance while showing the unity of the shop floor workers with the implied suggestion that it was the foremen who should 'Get on with it'. Gilley returned to his machine while Jack asked, "So you're looking for a job?"

"Yeh I s'pose so."

"'Ow are you with a chisel? See this pin?" - touching a six inch diameter, foot long shining steel shaft with a head shaped like a rivet. "D'you think you can cut an 'alf round oil-way in that with an 'ammer an' chisel without makin' too much of a pig's ear of it?"

"Hmm, I think I could do that all right, but I've only got measuring tools."

"You put it in the vice then, and I'll get an 'ammer 'n chisel." Coming back with the tools he pencilled a couple of lines on the pin and, offering me a half round chisel with a two-pound hammer, said, "Okay, then, let's see what you can do. Foller them lines an' keep it lookin' tidy." He watched for a minute or two then left me to carry on. When lunchtime came, I'd cut oil ways in three big grab hinge-pins.

ؼؼؼؼ

34

The Canteen

It's 12-noon September 5th 1964.

At the sound of a hooter we file past the punch clock, clocking out, then back into the canteen. I'm sitting beside Jack. I've learnt his surname's Butler. I'm wary because of Butler in the trade school. Gilley's there too and another fitter called Big Jim, to differentiate him from Scots Jim. He's quite young but big and quiet - and a little Scots labourer called Whulleh. That's Scottish for Willy, derived from Wee Willy.

The room's cleaners have an affinity with dirt. On the hard composition tiled floor grey trails indicate the cursory passage of dirty

97

mops that have dressed table legs in socks of greasy black muck, of a kind peculiar to engineering works. Smooth, gloss, cream walls vary in colour from light yellow with pale condensation streaks to heavily streaked nicotine brown. One wall is pierced with steel framed windows, opaqued with running condensation. Two are fitted with vent fans, louvres partially blocked with small horizontal stalactites of greasy dirt, built up over years of expelling damp greasy air. It's stark, unadorned. I grit my teeth to the chalk-on-a-blackboard scrape and clatter of fifty men's metal chairs on a hard floor. A babble of voices bounces and echoes between bare damp walls, accentuating the barren, jail-cell nature of the place.

The serving area looks cleaner but the food warmed in a big bain-marie looks pitifully unappetising - flaccid chips slumped one upon another and haricot beans in thin congealing tomato sauce. The pinnacle of culinary delight is reached with spam fritters, cheap spam slices, tinned relics of American food imported during the war, dipped in batter and deep-fried in old fat, producing a foul-tasting greasy blob. There is a further choice, tough-skinned sausages with innards of bread, gristly fat, the odd bone-chip and cheap chemical flavouring topped off with burnt lard. This delectable menu is served by unenthusiastic frowsy women whose sloppy dowdiness sets off the sad food. I'm immediately accepted as a fellow unfortunate, condemned to do time in this horrible place.

Butler asks, "Why 'ave they sent you 'ere then? They only send the outcasts 'ere. You don't look daft so you 'ave to be either crackers or trouble. We're on a sort of desert island 'ere. Bit like Alcatraz 'cept them bastards dun' 'ave to work. What do you recon you are? The little ones are often the worst trouble, like terriers. Is that you, a terrier? 'Ave you seen another little bloke? 'E's a welder. 'E's shorter than you. You wanna watch out for 'im. 'E's a terrier and crackers as well. Trevor's 'is name."

Gilley interjects "How did the lad get on Jack?"

"Oh 'e'll be OK doing the work. Rancy's taken a bit of a fancy to 'im though so we'll 'ave to be careful," with a knowing grin.

"Aye. Well, I think he'll be all right Jack. He's already told them to stuff crownwheels. Ah'm no' surprised to hear you thought that was bad, lad. Ah've heard tell the operators there have been using the pitch that contractors were putting on the roof, to pour onto their flywheels to speed up the machines. It's been wearing out the tools quicker so maintenance have been having to go faster replacing tools. It's fine for the operators. They've been hitting their targets early, but it's meant the maintenance section have been bloody near killing themselves trying to keep up.

I don't doubt the foremen were happy though; you'll find out soon enough - they try to run this place on the divide and rule principle. That's what the merit pennies are all about. You'll learn about them before long. They use them so no one knows who's earning what. The crafty bastards try to split us up all the time and make us suspicious of one another, as well as of them. Ah would ney mind if it didn't work, but it does. No one here trusts anyone and it's all about money. The first thing tay remember in this place, lad, is that money's no' everything."

It's surprising that the sentiments of Gilley are so much at odds with the general atmosphere of the room. It's so ugly that any act of kindness seems out of place. I won't eat in here often, even though the company of the other men is okay. Rather sandwiches and an apple in the workshop, dirtier but the dirt is honest working dirt, unlike this greasy muckiness.

***

In days that followed I made it my habit to eat my lunch in the workshop and soon joined Wyatt at the dartboard. Occasionally I won, but only when he either let me or gave me huge advantages. He was an excellent player and I nothing better than average.

For nearly four weeks I'd been doing bench-work in the workshop while I 'settled in,' when Big Jim walked into the shop, looking grim. "Butler's copped it again. We were jacking up the

99

bogie on the unloader crane. It bounced off the rails again at the hinge. Bloody crane's knackered. The job was going fine and then the toe on one of the jacks snapped off and whacked Jack in the face. Hit him like the ricochet from a bullet. It looks as though he might be done for. We found a piece of bone about as big as a matchstick. We think it was from his nose. It was in his hat. It took half an hour to get him down and he was still unconscious when they put him in the ambulance."

∾∾∾∾

35

We're bought by weight.

It's 7.30 a.m., December 5th 1964.

I've worked at the furnace for three months now, each day wheeling my bike from the garden shed, through the house, where white, gloss painted, bumpy brick walls of our tiny kitchen glisten with running condensation. The wood at the bottom of the windowpanes is lined with black mould where it meets the glass, from its daily soaking with condensation. Mum cuts bread for sandwiches and Dad's porridge is steaming on the stove. The room is clammy warm, the windows fogged from the kettle boiled for Dad's shave, and from the porridge steamer. I'll have time for some porridge too, today. I'm a bit early. Opening the back door lets in a shock of cold air, bringing goose pimples to bare arms, accustomed to the steamy, morning-start, atmosphere.

I ride the three and a half miles to the factory with seventeen thousand other day-shift men, all descending on the factory, racing to beat the clock. The road is flat, apart from the last half mile - that's the bridge over the railway shunting yards. My record for the trip is eight minutes. Occasionally traffic lights at the main gate fail and police direct the traffic. This is every-body's nightmare, coppers included - they get sworn at. The air's blue with exhaust smoke and bad language. The coppers can be forced off the road by frustrated workers and get laughed at as they stand in a line at the kerb, taking numbers of the law-breakers pouring into work with gleeful disregard for the impotent scribbling arms of the law. The scramble to the car parks is anarchy. Everyone is late, and it can take days to get production running smoothly again.

I don't want to be there, and cut it as fine as possible. Three minutes late and I lose a quarter of an hour's pay - three times late in a month and I lose the job. Striking the right balance is critical. The road into the factory begins at one end of the old village. No longer a village, thirty years ago it was engulfed by the housing estate to accommodate thirty thousand employees needed for 'labour' at the factory.

'Labour'. It used to mean work, but now, it can mean people as an adjunct to a machine, or a system. 'Get some more labour in' is a phrase they use, referring to us employees. We're bought by weight.

Our department is operated so that we, in the main workshop, carry out work in all the plants related to the blast furnace. Some areas have resident fitters, and we provide support when major jobs come up or serious breakdowns create a demand for extra 'labour'. In the past three months I've worked quite successfully in several of the plants. The foreman, Frank Rance, has decided to station me permanently in the coke ovens bye-products with Bernie, the resident fitter there, who is generally regarded as the best in the department. The plant is the most technically sophisticated. If there is a particularly intractable problem with a machine anywhere in the department, it's Bernie who is called to trouble shoot.

101

36

Christmas

Christmas Eve 1964 11.00 a.m:

Walking through the factory. The lines are running slower than usual and engines come past with graffiti scrawled on them 'Merry Xmas to all our drivers', and 'All I want for Christmas is a new head.' There's a dry wit somewhere. There are balloons tied to some of the machines and cigarette salesmen have been allowed in to dish out free cigarettes. There is an unaccustomed smell of cigars. It's the first time I'd ever felt a tolerable atmosphere in the place - even the foremen look relaxed.

***

A few of us from the furnace workshop are in the pub after work. I'm sitting next to Bernie who I've met a few times. I like him - there's an openness about him and a sense of fun as well as humour. I don't know how it came about, but conversation has got around to Christmases past and Velucci, who's had a drop more than's good for him, is telling tales of his worst Christmas driving a bulldozer in Korea, burying the bodies of Chinese soldiers in mass graves. He describes them:

"Coming in waves almost like the fucking sea. Our lot just cut 'em down with machine guns, almost like hosing them down, then I had to start work. Happy fucking Christmas."

Bernie lightens things up. "My best Christmas was in Northern India. They'd just let me out of the glasshouse and the army being the army they put me in charge of the stores at a rest and recreation centre up in the mountains. There was a major in charge but he was pissed all the time, so he didn't even count. What a joke - I'd been in for fraud so they put me in charge of stores. I'd been a sergeant in the pay corps and doing a bit of fiddling and lost my stripes for the second

102

time. They were so disorganised, it was even worse than across the road. We had everything: plenty of booze, plenty of food and lots of servants. There were Sherpas who could carry anything up the mountains. They had enlarged hearts due to carrying massive loads. I've seen one of those blokes carry a baby grand piano on his back. They died when they were about forty 'cos of their enlarged hearts. They more or less burst or something.

"I'd managed to get hold of a dozen pay books and was collecting wages for the lot of them. I lived like a prince. The blokes used to wonder why I always laughed if anyone put 'The Hall of the Mountain King' on the gramophone. I used to think I was the mountain king. On top of that there were other fiddles. I fixed up hot showers and used to charge for soap. You'd be surprised what I used to make out of that. I made them give me their caps before they got their shower so I always got paid. I came out of there with a real nice nest egg, then lost the lot, apart from a few gemstones, when we crashed going into Ceylon. That was my ticket home. What a price for a ticket home, two ribs, the dearest plastic surgery nose in England and eighteen months in hospital. The nurses were something special though. They were told they were part of our treatment because you scare yourself when you see your face with your eyes looking out from something that looks as though its been through a mincer. I had a stainless steel bolt through my nose for a few weeks. They were supposed to try to convince us we still looked okay. I looked worse than Frankenstien."

"Nothing changes," says Big Jim who gets fed up with Bernie's tales of India.

"The nurses weren't rude like some people," says Bernie with a sharp smile at Jim. "I was sore a lot of the time cos' they were taking strips off my bum to stick on my face but it was almost worth it for the treatment we got from those nurses. I could put up with plenty of that all right." (He's lost two ribs in the crash and now has to take three months off each year to avoid losing his army pension.) "It's good to be home but that place was beautiful. Christmas time there; I was pissed for a week. If it got too cold you could just ride down the mountain a bit to where it was warmer. Too hot and up you'd go to where it's cooler. I could live there. It's a lot better than this dump. Food's better too. A nice curry knocks boiled beef and carrots into a cocked hat."

"D'you think it's much different now it's not British any more?" I ask.

"Oh I doubt it's that different, it'll still be run by the same crooks that ran it then. Maybe the Hindus and Muslims might be a bit more at one another's throats but I shouldn't think that'd make a fat lot of difference. If you earned what we do now, living's so cheap you'd be rich. I could live like a king again on my pension."

Bernie likes to give the impression he's a knowing slick spiv but he's far too funny and smiles too much to be convincing. His pencil moustache looks as though it belongs on someone else.

"At least you've got a pension. The wife of one of those blokes who fell off the furnace when they opened it last year lives three doors up from us, and still hasn't had a penny, and she's got his two kids to look after. We're having them round on Boxing Day but we've not got a lot to spare. They'll not be having much of a Christmas." Big Jim, who normally says little and is a bit too serious, obviously has this on his mind.

Brown, the assistant shop steward, leans forward, saying, "Well it looks as though the main factory will be striking again in the New Year unless some magic happens over the holiday to empty the stock car parks."

This sets Gilley off on a bitter tirade. Brown seems to annoy him, in a way, more than the management. "Aye, well the AEU's in the pocket of management. Until the union and the government are one, we're pissing into the wind. Joe Stalin may have been a bastard, but at least he was our bastard. The Labour Party in the end's just a waste of time. When the unions got recognition of the TUC by the Government in 1916 the Labour Party was there. I was just a boy when they had the tanks on the streets of Glasgow. It was more

104

important for them to fight us than the Germans then. That was the thin end of the wedge. When all's said and done, the Labour Party is just the sad creature of the Tories, and Militant'll no' change that, even if they really wanted to." Brown says "Piss off, Gilley. It's fucking Christmas and what about the NHS anyway?"

"Aye Labour gave us the NHS, but that was just a sop to stop the rot they saw coming from Russia. Why d'you think Labour's helping the yanks hang on to Berlin. Their bastard Churchill sold this country to the Yanks wi' 'lease lend', aye and Scotland too. Our local MP – the right dishonourable Tom Driberg - our very own representative of the Labour Party in Parliament, what is he? - A bloody degenerate. He's William Hickey the muckraker in the *Daily Mail*. The only Christmas present I'd give him would a trip under a ten-ton Routemaster and Ah'd pity the poor bugger who had to wash the filth off the tyres. Any self-respecting working man would be sickened at the thought of walking through the door of the *Mail*, let alone working there. He used to be in the Communist Party but we threw him out because he was a stool pigeon for MI5. He's got the morals of a poxed-up snake. He does na' represent me. Ah'd no gi' him the honour o' ma' spit," the power of his emotion causing his accent to broaden.

Having concluded this speech, the dryness created merits the sinking of half his pint in one great gulp. "Happy Hogmanay," he says, planting his mug firmly on the table. He's asserting his Scottishness among these soft misguided Sassenachs.

This harangue dumbfounds both Banks, the steward, and Brown, who says, "Well you can't deny that Labour has made things better with the National Health." Thereafter politics is carefully avoided and the conversation drifts into other areas. Bernie whispers to me with quiet grin. "If either Gilley or Bank's lot ever get in, they'll tear us all apart and then one another for an encore.

37

An Ordinary Day?

Monday January 4th 1965 7.56 a.m:

Christmas is gone - still nearly another dragging three years to go before the bloody apprenticeship's finished, but I'm working with Bernie now, and we get on well. Things are better. Bernie plays the system to the limit and he has two advantages: first, he's better at the job than anyone else in the plant; and second he has his war pension and can use his disability as a weapon against the management.

We're chatting by the punch clock. I'm rolling a fag. It's Monday and echoes of ships' horns on the river are whipped away on a wind that's made of freezing needles. Shoulders are hunched as it pierces winter clothes, despite the shelter of the punch clock hut. We wait till the last minute before we go in and wriggle into thick grey-blue cotton boiler suits, ready to start the day's work. Because it's Monday, our boiler suits will be clean - that is, they have a horrible chemical cleaner smell rather than stinking of old sweat and older grease.

The day is grey, cold, bleak, January. Dawn has just broken. The mood is downcast. Fred, the skinny rigger, with rotten teeth and smelly breath, lightens the atmosphere a little. "Best day of my life, our Eileen got the letter this morning. She got seven 'O' Levels, with good grades as well, and I finished paying for the car." Bernie says with a wry smile, "Pleased someone's got something to be glad about in this shit-hole. I think my head gasket's gone." The clock clanks another minute; the numerals show eight. Charlie, the other rigger, is still a hundred yards away and wheezily jogging to reach the clock in time. A hand takes his card and clocks him in. Someone shouts, "Come on you old git, or you'll lose a quarter." "Well clock me in, you rotten bastards." Another shout, "Run you old bugger," to general laughter. Stamping out our dog ends, we file into the plant. It's rare to start the day on a happy note. The conversation is usually far more depressing, especially on a bitter grey Monday morning in January.

***

The apprenticeship is said to be the best apart from the Post Office - in a way it is. They teach us to do the job well. The library is one of the best engineering libraries in the world, and they make a point of telling us that any engineering book we want, they will get, even if it costs hundreds of pounds.

So why is it so awful?

The men are a genial lot. There is something though, the essence of the place. There is a saying that they use: 'In the trade school we teach you the right way - then we teach you the fast way.' That is at the heart of the problem, everything is done on the basis of expediency. 'Just get it going' is the attitude. I might only be mending a pump, but my work is a physical expression of me, and I do the best job I can. I take pride in the work I do; take that pride away, and I'm nothing.

There is only one objective for them ... money. To retain one's self-respect, it is paramount to do a job that you are proud of; take away the stamp of individuality, and you are utterly humiliated. Why else do jailers shave heads and put prisoners in uniform? Sacrifice pride in the work you do for money, and you lose your humanity. Walk through the gate here, and you become a number; clocking in is a humiliation. I'm T1052. It could be worse. It could be tattooed on my arm - or my forehead.

***

We're walking along the road behind a big fork truck. The forks are raised eighteen feet, as high as they can go, and separated as wide as the machine allows. Balanced across the forks is forty feet of railway line. It weighs three tons, and more than fills the width of the road.

107

As the truck lumbers along over bumps, the ends of the railway line bounce two or three feet in the air. Frank Rance, the foreman in charge, asks "Did any of you phone the security to make sure that the road is closed." Bernie, my boss, says, "I did better than that. I sent Dave to tell the man on the gate why the road's closed and put up a proper sign."

"Good" is the only reply. Just at that moment, Ted, our labourer, makes a grab for the end of the railway line as it jumps higher than usual when the forktruck goes over a pot hole. 'Thunk,' the line lands, with Ted still clutching the end. The truck continues its lumbering progress. Ted turns, his eyes wide - two fingers are hanging by threads of skin, almost completely severed. He stands and stares at his mangled hand in shocked incomprehension.

"Fuck. Get him down the medical and call an ambulance," yells Frank.

"Stop... Stop." He's yelling at the truck driver, who is already carefully slowing to avoid further mishaps with his perilous load. "Put it down. We'll have to drag the fucking thing."

"Should have done that in the first place. It wasn't my fault," says the driver.

Ted is sitting at the side of the road, still staring mesmerised at his dangling fingers, his face grey. "I'll go and get my car," says Bernie "and take him to the medical." "What the fuck did you do it for?" shouts Frank, also in a state of shock. "It weighs three tons."

"I just did it. I didn't think about it. It doesn't hurt," says Ted, now not properly conscious. Someone has ripped a whole emergency medical cabinet off the wall in the lab at the far end of the coke ovens, and is desperately pulling out all the cloth it contains to bind the crushed hand. Bernie arrives in his car, and Ted is bundled off to the medical department, where an ambulance is waiting.

Why did it happen? To try to move a forty foot length of railway-line that way was plain stupid. To drill a hole in one end or weld an eyebolt on would have been simple. Hook it to a tractor, tie it on to a couple of trolleys and it would have been easy to move and there'd have been no need to close the road. The whole operation would have been quicker, easier and safer. So why do it that way? The answer is simple:

> Rush, rush, rush.
> Don't think.
> Get the job done.
> Now, now, NOW!

These words are a liturgy in the minds of foremen who operate like automatons. Management is always there, waiting to pounce.

> Your job's on the line.
> Perform, or you're out.
> Get your arse in gear and
> GET THE FUCKING JOB DONE.
> D'you think you're in a holiday camp?
> Get the fucking job DONE.

Result - a mess. Ted's in hospital. The job has been put back hours, days even, and the whole department is buzzing with gnawing discontent. The real cause? .... attitude - the avaricious attitude of management and its total blindness to everything but the pursuit of ... money.

38

Bernie

I've worked with Bernie for a few weeks now. He's my boss and we get on really well. We've become friends. He likes cars, and owns a Humber Super Snipe estate. He's like a big kid with it. He's lowered the suspension, fitted wide wheels, and done a lot to the engine. It looks like a racing hearse. He's teaching me to drive, not in his car. He went with me to Seven Kings, where Broad, who knocked Sid out at school, has his car lot. There were hundreds of cars and he recommended my little Morris Thousand. Bernie thought it looked okay and it's not given any trouble so far. I'd have liked Mum's dad to have seen it. He'd have enjoyed it and been pleased for me. Mum's been in it, but it scares her rigid. Her knuckles are white all the time she's riding, which takes away all the pleasure from going anywhere with her. It's best to go on public transport. She calls buses her big red taxis.

We're based in the bye-products plant, across the road from the laboratory and the coke ovens that produce town gas and coke for the blast furnace. It's five minutes' walk from the main blast furnace workshop at the other end of the road, by the coke ovens where the canteen is. We don't usually go there; it's still a dump, and the food is disgusting as ever. The plant we maintain washes the gas, and extracts chemicals and impurities. All around is a chain-link fence topped with barbed wire, with a security hut at the gate, where a guard collects all our combustibles - matches, lighters, tobacco and cigarettes - in exchange for a token, because the atmosphere inside is so volatile any spark could cause an explosion. We all gladly comply.

We carry out chemical production processes here, making naphtha for mothballs, nitrate for fertilizer and explosives, benzol - a petrol fuel additive, tar, and a really nasty acid they call B.O.V. that doesn't affect skin but is absorbed through it and eats away at bones. It's said you wake up in the night in agony and the only cure is amputation. This is the source of a mythology of horror stories in the plant.

The appearance of the place is mildly 'science fiction,' with all sorts of rather weird looking vessels connected by pipes. Stainless steel parts glint in the sun as a counterpoint to general pipework, which is either lagged with asbestos, then given an outer coat of tarred felt, or simply painted black. Walk around and reciprocating pumps rattle and clatter whilst steam exhausts from machines with sudden hisses. Few people are employed here and the whole gives an eerie 'big brother' feeling of machines controlled by unseen hands elsewhere. Nothing grows; the ground underfoot is made from crushed slag from the blast furnace. It looks like grey glass. The atmosphere is poisonous; leave a penny overnight, in the open, and it'll be thoroughly tarnished by morning.

There are just four of us based here. Our workshop is quite small; two labourers help Bernie and me doing maintenance work when necessary, though they're classed as plant operators. There's a bench and a couple of vices, a bit of space for storage, and a long low bench where we can sit during breaks. The walls are dirty bare concrete and there are no windows, just a door opening onto a platform where rotary pumps hum. What they pump is pretty nasty, and the chemical stinks given off you don't want around, especially whilst you eat. Unless it's very hot, the door remains closed.

It's a quarter of a mile walk to the canteen, but both Bernie and I are keen to hear any news about this morning's events, and we're going to the canteen today to catch up on the gossip. Ada, a scruffy woman who serves lukewarm greasy food from under a crooked burst hairnet, asks with a simpering smile, "And what can I do you two strangers for?"

Bernie replies, "Just two teas please. Lord Rayleigh can keep the manure for his farms," with a smirking nod towards the evil smelling chips (Rayleigh's farms have the catering contract). "We do our best, there's no need to be rude," says Ada primly.

"Wasn't rude, just helping you cut out the middle-man. Chuck it straight down the bog, luv', where it belongs."

"If that's how you feel, I don't know why you come here."

"I just come for the titillating sight of your luscious body Ada, can't stay away."

"Piss off," says Ada, miffed at his sarcasm.

Sitting at a table occupied by two labourers, Bernie asks, "Any news of Ted?"

"Last we heard they were going to try to stitch his fingers back on, but they're such a mess that it's touch and go whether they'll take. Won't know, apparently, for a few days, but it didn't crush the joints, just the actual bones, so they may be okay. He was at the hospital quick, so it looks promising. Even if he keeps his fingers, though, they won't be much use, 'cos the tendons are all mashed. In a way he was lucky, it was just the last two fingers of his left hand and he's right handed."

"Some fuckin' luck."

Stan, the top labourer, holding up the paper he's reading, points to an article headlined,

'POLICE UNION CALLS FOR INCREASED PAY.'

"They're asking for more money cos' it's a dangerous job – huh."

"Yeh and you know what makes it dangerous," says Bernie, "It's us. They should come and try working here, then they'd find out what dangerous is. Look at that," gesturing with his cup towards a dirty cardboard 'Safety Shield' with a chart underneath displaying statistics of the various departments' last month's safety record.

"Talk about take the piss. No major injuries last month. Just the odd broken arm, rib, or leg, nothing you wouldn't get over. No mention of Jock McIntyre. His leg was crushed between the buffers up on the high-line two years ago. It's never healed right up since. I was talking to him the other day. They've given him a strap-on leather gaiter to keep it straight. He said it's fucking agony. He's told them he thinks he'd be better without it and a peg leg. He's going to see another specialist soon. No mention of that on the fucking 'Safety

112

Shield.' Be interesting to see how it reads next month; we've not seen the last of that railway line yet."

So even the labourers know that to deal with that length of railway line is DANGEROUS. Roll it over and it wriggles like a snake, a three-ton snake that'll take your foot off in one swift, deadly bite.

❦❦❦❦

39

This is no way to carry on.

Tuesday January 5th 1965 8.30 a.m:

I've been 'lent' to the main workshop today to help on the railway line job. I'm on the crane where the line is to be fitted. The bogie has come off the rails twice since Jack Butler got his face smashed. It can take several men a day to get it back on the rails. It weighs over twenty-five tons and is over a hundred feet above the river. The management made the job of fitting the new rails a priority and Ted's fingers were crushed in the rush. Some of the men are saying the job is jinxed, others are saying it's Jack Butler. He's been involved in three major accidents while he's worked here and some are superstitiously blaming him as some kind of Jonah. One thing is sure, no-one wants to work on the rail job on the unloader-crane.

On a clear day you can see St Pauls fifteen miles away (Clear days don't come often. We churn out enough muck to dirty the atmosphere on any but the windiest, freshest of days). Along the banks of the river the scenery is bleak industrial, with tanks, jetties, wharves and cranes; hardly a tree to be seen. A strong smell of Demerara sugar is carried on the wind from the dock next door, where a bulk carrier is unloading. Grabs swinging, opening, dropping, closing, huge dribbling mouths, gobbling hundreds of tons of the stuff

113

every hour.

We're high above the water; it's black, except where ripples glitter, reflecting the cold, weak, winter sun, low in the mountain cold blue sky. I struggle against an icy northeast wind, roaring up the funnel of the river, so strong, it feels as though someone's on the other side of the driver's cab door, pulling hard against me. The sweet sugar smell is queer, so much at odds with the cold that makes my teeth ache as I breathe through my mouth. Squeezed inside the cab, in a cosy fug, are Charley and Fred, the two riggers.

"Fucking great day for it," I say. "Mind you, it could be snowing.'

"Give it time," says Fred, who last week celebrated paying off the car and his daughter's 'O' levels.

"Where's Bernie?"

"He played the war wounds card. Crafty bastard's working on an acid pump, in the warm, in the bye-products workshop. Told Rancey his back was bad again. Makes you almost wish you had a war pension."

"Can't blame him. I'd do the same if I was him. This railway line job's one to stay away from. It's a right bastard. It's fuckin' mad, trying to fit it up here in one lump, and this weather doesn't help. It should have been brought up in bits, then welded back together, if they must have it without fishplates."

"Rancey was here yesterday, hopping about like my three year old when she needs a piss. We told him to fuck off and leave us alone or we're off the job."

"He doesn't know anything about engineering, let alone rigging. He's a worse nag than his old woman and she's driving him to the nuthouse. Spend, spend, spend. Nag, nag, nag. I pity the poor bastard. One thing though, don't let him get too near you on this job. You need all the wits you've got up here, without that twat prattin' around behind you."

***

114

So what's going on? The men are asserting their right to do the job as they see fit. The foreman accepts that this is as it should be. Is this delegation? No. The men are working independently of the foreman. They understand the job better than he does. Why is he there?

There's something amiss here. Something odd's going on. I feel angry and resentful, a feeling bubbling away in my head all the time in this place. The only way to vent this anger is at management. Frank Rance represents them. At a personal level I feel pity for the poor bloke. He gets more money than me, but not that much. His personal life is a mess, his wife rides him like a donkey, and he puts up with jibes from the men, all day, every day. He's got vertigo so bad he can't stand on an upturned bucket without getting into a panic, and half the jobs in this place involve working high above the ground. It really is possible he'll finish up in the madhouse. He has sold his self-respect, and is hardly a person worthy of consideration, even by himself. He's chosen his side, and he must accept the consequences. It's them or us. 'You pays your money and you takes your choice.' There's no room for sentiment here.

***

We're on the top of the crane now, and it's high - a hundred and twenty feet when the tide's in. I drop a bolt and watch the second hand on my watch ... One... Two... Three... splash. I can see the splash, but not hear it above the roar of the wind. Three seconds ... a hell of a long time to be falling. One hand for me and one for the job.

We've got safety harnesses, but you can't keep them clipped on all the time. Sometimes there's nothing to clip to, and you have to move around to do the job.

Fred and Charley are up here. We have to shout to communicate because of the noise of the wind. There's another man here, Ernie. He knows the job all right, but he's sixty-two, and suffers from arthritis. He's not fit for this sort of work. He only carries on working here to buy cigarettes from Parker, a wheeler dealer who runs a cash and carry business 'on the side' in the factory. Ernie sells the cigarettes he buys around the workshop and in his shop, in the middle of the estate, that his wife runs during the day.

The railway line is up here. Fred and Charley did that yesterday. God knows how they managed it. They've supported it at four points to stop it bowing too much. The ropes are still on; we've got to jack it up bit by bit, to get the ropes off, and then because it's on its side, we have to roll it over. This is the nasty bit.

"We'll start at the end that's over the water," yells Fred, naturally taking charge. We're all aware that organizing this sort of job is best left to one man. He'll then have a structure in his mind, of how the work will be done. If two people have different ideas as to how to finish the thing, you can end up working against one another; this job's dangerous enough, without that sort of nonsense. Fred's a good man, with lots of experience, so we let him run the show.

"Dave - you go and get some bits of wood for packing, about a foot long, and an inch thick, as many as you can carry."

I'm the youngest and fittest and I'll do the running around. There are about seventy steps to the ground. I'll be keeping fit today. At least that'll keep me warm. It's bloody freezing up here. I'm back with the packing, puffing from the climb. They're ready for me.

Fred asks, jigging around and rubbing his hands, "What kept you, idle little bleeder? We've been freezing our bollocks off up here waiting for you."

"I had to stop for a cup of tea, cos' I was cold as well, then my bladder shrank, cos' I was so cold, so I had to go for a piss. After that I came as quick as I could".

"Cheeky sod. Get on with it." He's grinning; he knows I was as quick as I could be. They've already got a couple of jacks under the first ten feet of line, and we start inserting the packing pieces. I've only been up here five minutes and my fingers are already numb with cold. This is bad. You can cut yourself when your fingers are this cold, and not even know. Your grip becomes unsure - DANGER.

116

The line is packed up and as straight as we can get it. We're equipped with levers to hook on the line, ready to roll it over. We're all watching Fred; he gives a nod, and we start to pull. Steady, it's coming. Ready, balance; ready to hop back out of its way as it rolls. Fuck, it's going back, someone's stopped pulling. I can't carry on against it... It'll take me with it... I have to let go... The lever sails head over heels into the hopper below.

A yell... I can hear above the roar of the wind and from the corner of my eye I see Fred's hand disappear into the void... Jesus... Jesus.

I'm panting, only part through exertion. I turn and look over the handrail, just in time to see him hit the water.

Three seconds? Three minutes? Three hours?

He's face down, spreadeagled.

I'm running to the steps, down, down. Trip, nearly fall.

I'm on the ground, running to the edge of the jetty.

There's no sign of Fred. Two welders are already watching; one has a lifebelt. The tide is in full flow, angry water, zipping past at ten miles an hour. His head appears. We're running to keep up. The aim is good - the belt actually hits him. There's no response, but his head moves almost as though he's swimming.

The other welder, it's Blunt, has stepped out of his boots; he throws off his leather apron and dives. Shit.... It'll kill him as well. The water must be just above freezing.

There's a dinghy tied to one of the piles. I've been in it before, with contractors working on the piles. I climb down the ladder, start the tiny engine and set off. I'm shaking and I feel sick. Fred's head disappears and resurfaces intermittently. Blunt has given up the chase and is swimming towards the jetty. I'm in two minds whether to stop and try to pick him up.

I think Fred's dead.

I think he's... dead.

The engine on the boat isn't powerful enough to beat the tide. I couldn't pick up Blunt if I wanted. So follow...

Follow what? Fred's... body.

God!

Thank heaven... Someone's called the River Police. They've seen me. They're racing towards me. There's his head again. I point - I think they've seen it.

Yes, yes - they're moving towards it. Slowing down. Bloody hell it's gone down again. They're still following. That's it, they've got it. Now they're coming for me. They've got the painter and I'm being pulled onto their boat.

God! That's Fred. My God, that's Fred.

I'm still shaking and shivering at the same time, half numb with cold. I feel awful.

And Eileen got seven 'O' Levels and he'd just finished paying for the car.

Bastards.... bastards.

I keep seeing that hand clutching at air.

This isn't a job, it's a fucking war zone.

What's going on?

Whatever it is, it's got to stop.

This is no way to carry on.

***

Home. "What are you doing home at this time of day?" It's my mother. She's just scrubbed the step outside and I scrub my wet feet on the coir mat that's slowly disintegrating by the front door. The lino's polished, spotless. She's just moved on to cleaning that. I can smell Johnson's Wax.

"One of the blokes I was working with got killed today. He fell off a crane and I helped fish him out of the river."

"Oh."

I take three steps down the hall, and pause at the kitchen door, partly to feel the solidity of the doorknob. I'm feeling, not dizzy, kind of detached, as though everything is far away.

118

"I'm going to have a cup of tea. D'you want one?"

"I was just going to your grandmother's. You know we have to keep an eye on her, it's my turn today."

"Right."

"What are you going to do? Do they know you've come home?"

"Yeh, I clocked out. Loads of the blokes were packing up."

"What are you going to do?"

"I'll probably read."

"Are you alright?"

"Yeh I'm okay."

"All right then, I'm going to your grandmother's."

She's gone, but I'm not all right. I keep seeing that hand disappearing. Head bobbing, freezing water passing the boat and.... and Fred. I feel weird. I make tea, attempting to regain a feeling of normality. Milk first, not too much. I don't like too much milk. Reminds me of school playtimes. Water's boiled. One for me and one for the pot, just like on the adverts. Boring crap adverts. Pour, stir, hmm - good tea, commonplace, ordinary.

I take the tea to the living room. Tidy - everything in its place. Mum makes this place a shrine to tidiness and stability. What a life, nothing to do but look after us and keep things on the straight and narrow. What a waste. She can't really relate to what I'm saying, so she treats it as though I'd said I'd been shopping. Treat the unaccustomed with aplomb, nonchalance even, and then at least it feels like something we can deal with.

I pick up a book, *Zane Grey*, one of Dads interminable cowboys. How on earth can he keep reading this tripe? I drop it carelessly, then pick it up again and put it away tidily. I understand and appreciate, more than ever before, the effort and sacrifice my mother makes to keep the place and us in order. I'm feeling better. At least there's some kind of sanity here.

40

Where to Start

I hated the place before, but now I was gripped by a kind of madness. I wanted to hit out. I felt like running around smashing things and punching the people who gave orders. Looking back, I wasn't aware of how much my involvement in the events that led to and followed Fred's death affected me. Now I was always aware that unwanted images might slip into my consciousness, fetching with them guilt, anger, frustration and hate for the system and those who created it. I couldn't talk about things going on inside my head. How can you describe a jumble of disconnected feelings and images? I tried to partition off the part of my mind that, at any moment, might throw up disturbing pictures I didn't want to see.

Something positive comes of the worst of events. I began to try to understand what was really going on. What was it that made these awful events almost commonplace? My view of the world changed. I've never believed in a god who sits, on some sort of throne, in Heaven - one minute causing a spider to run down aunt's cleavage, and the next creating a hurricane to kill thousands in the West Indies. There's no divine plan laying out our lives for us. Einstein's view, that God doesn't gamble, just proves that genius in one sphere may not be reflected in another. Chaos theory shows there is only serendipity.

I have always thought there is some kind of human spirit, but that gives me no reason to believe that there is life after death. What the hell difference would it make if there was? Why should we be here a first time, much less a second? If there is some sort of 'Deus ex machina,' the question always remains, what created it?

I learnt that nothing is simple and many of our problems we create ourselves. Our ghosts aren't something spiritual. They don't wander around old houses with their heads under their arms. We create our own ghosts, and let them wander in our heads, making us frightened in old houses, of heights, or repulsed at the sight of porridge. They contribute to the way we mould the truth, which is our own creation. Two people standing in the same spot, at the same time, see entirely different things. Before the accident my world existed in sharp monochrome, everything was black and white, and easy to deal with, no ghosts, no demons. If you don't like dogs crapping on the pavement - shoot the dogs. If you don't like the smoke - douse the fire.

જ્ઞજ્ઞજ્ઞજ્ઞ

41

Different Me.

Wednesday January 6th 1965 6.30 a.m:

My truth today is different to yesterday's. I feel a burning anger and the first inkling of why I feel a need to change things. I'm not a cog or a bearing. I'm not a part of a machine. I'm a human being with senses and emotions. There are things that are important to me outside of cash in my pocket, a home to go to, food in my belly, some nooky, and a couple of pints at the weekend. My ghosts are new and working overtime. I don't rule out violence. I don't rule out anything. Action would be cathartic, a means of blotting out the distracting dreadful images. It's clear though that real answers lie not just in action but in understanding.

At one level I can communicate as well as most. I couldn't have made my feelings clearer than when I treated the teachers with contempt by saying 'thank you' when I was caned. Now I realise I need something back. Contempt is a one-way street, just negative, salvaging my pride, but that's all. To understand, I need to communicate, and for that I need to take as well as give. At school a

121

couple of teachers truly tried their best, giving freely of themselves, though most were largely apathetic. The lives of the apathetic were arid. The ones who gave most were the ones who gained most, not necessarily in cash, but in the sheer joy of living. I could tell they were the happiest, the least fearful.

Here it's worse, much worse. Employees are encouraged to be single mindedly selfish and greedy. In this atmosphere real education is impossible because the true objective has been lost. The view of education I'm beginning to stumble upon has to relate to the whole of humanity - not the limited, blinkered, understanding, commonly promoted as education today. I'm not good at that anyway. That's why I'm here in the first place. That's why I failed the eleven plus exam. I didn't need, or want, the sort of education valued by them, the discipline of a narrow science, that sets out to give great understanding of a detail, of a tiny piece of the jigsaw. I want an overview, a way of seeing the world that enables me to understand how it's organized; then there might be some chance of changing it for the better.

I need an insight, first into history. It's not difficult to work out that we can't understand what's going on now without an understanding of what led us here. Before building a rocket, it helps to have built a steam engine. I need to understand economics; get to grips with how things have changed in the past and why. I start to read but flounder, blundering through books in no sort of order. Too much to do. I need pointers. I have a problem - where to start?

42

The Syndicate & The Devil

Monday January 11th 1965 8.00 a.m:

At the punch-clock hut by the gate to the by-products plant,

"Hello, Bernie. What's been happening? what's happening about Fred's Missis?"

"I don't know anything. You know what happened, you helped get him out, didn't you?"

"Yeah, I just followed him on the tide, in the jetty dinghy, 'til the police launch came. I was fucking freezing, and I felt terrible, then they dragged me onto their boat, and I saw him; he didn't really look human. I've been thinking about it all weekend. He looked awful." I'm near to tears. Bernie, embarrassed, doesn't know what to say - there's an awkward silence. Some of the others have come along. Polish Ted, one of the operators who's told me horrific stories about what happened to him during the war, when he was a boy, says, "Blunt is still in the hospital; they pump his stomach but they say he be okay. He suffer from exposure, but he be okay." I've more or less regained my composure.

"What happened after I went?" I ask.

"Fucking Gallatia got Wilko' to ask for volunteers to put up safety nets under the bogie on the crane. Talk about shut the gate after the horse has bolted. No one from here would do it. Most of them went home as a mark of respect. They got some Italian bastard Fratelli or something's his name, not even a foreman, just a charge-hand from the foundry and some other blokes; no one seems to know where they came from, to do it. According to the rumours that are going around, Gallatia's after insurance money. God knows what'll happen to Fred's wife."

"What about his daughter - she just got seven 'O' levels - did he have any other kids? Is his Missis okay? How's Ted getting on? is he going to keep his fingers?"

No one knows anything for sure. Another workday begins, with the detested clock showing eight. Bernie and me start work cleaning a De Laval Purifier. It's a centrifuge. It's being used to separate coke dust from the tar that's a by-product of the coal used to make the coke for the furnace. It's a dirty job but routine, and there's no pressure. We chat as we work.

"How can Gallatia get away with putting nets on the crane after Fred fell in the river? It's daft. Fred wouldn't have gone in if there had been nets, and surely the insurance company will make some kind of enquiry to find out what happened .... if there'd been nets Fred'd be okay."

"What do you know about the syndicate?"

"I've heard a bit but what's that got to do with Fred?"

"The syndicate is big in this factory. All sorts of people are involved, nobody really knows who does what. Parker knows more than most, but Parker's not the top dog. (Everyone knows about Parker. He runs the Cash & Carry where Ernie is buying his cigarettes. It's crossed my mind that Ernie stopped pulling on the railway line. The pain from his arthritis could have caused it.) There are people in the management who know what's going on. Gallatia must know what Parker's up to. I think Gallatia's up to his eyes in fiddles. Some of the security men are as bent as meat skewers and there must be people on the outside involved. Last month someone made a cock-up and ordered a ton of split pins. They went into the furnace. Someone with pull made a really stupid balls-up and got away with it. Why? Because they had pull. If you or me made a cock up half as daft as that we'd be out of the gate so fast we wouldn't see it, but if we were in the syndicate it could be forgotten, just like those split pins."

"You know you can get a car with good papers from Parker so there have to be people at the DVLA involved and Parker hasn't got the style to manage that. Some of the big parts for the cars built outside the factory go into the Westminster tip barges as they go past the jetty. Watch the Babcock and Wilcox crane. They drop the bits in as they go past. Half the blokes on the jetty must be getting a cut. When a thing's that big, greasing the palm of an insurance loss adjuster is a piece of cake. You know half the blokes in this place are nicking. You've been through the gate when the 'security' have a purge. You can hardly walk for the nicked bits on the floor by the gate. No one's got any conscience about taking from the Company because everybody who works here knows that from Henry Ford down 'Company men' are all thieving, robbing, bastards. They've sold their souls to the devil and Henry Ford the flaming second is the fuckin' devil. We all know that dear old Henry couldn't give a monkey's about us, or anyone else, as long as he makes the maximum amount of cash. You only have to look at the day they opened the new furnace; the painters were dropping off with carbon monoxide poisoning; and sweet old Henry carried on cutting the ribbon, even while there were blokes dead and dying lying on the ground."

"But there must be something we can do?"

"You can't do anything. The union's bent. They're owned by the Company and England owes America for all those tanks they sold us during the war - and Fords made lots of the tanks. You know the story. Rolls Royce did the design of the Spitfire engine and Fords made it. There were more Rolls Royce Merlin engines made in this plant than at Rolls Royce. If Fords pulls out of England then there'll be nothing to rob. We'll all be fucked. The only thing to do would be to join Russia and what have they got in Russia? They've got fuck all except Stalin and he's keeping order by keeping everybody shit scared and half starved to death. You've heard the joke about Brigitte Bardot. If she walked down the main street in Moscow with nothing on but a pair of good shoes, the blokes would all be looking at her shoes 'cos a pair of shoes in Moscow would buy you a slice of Brigitte herself. That's really no joke. Just ask Polish Ted about life in fuckin' Russia. We think things are rough here. They're still living in holes in the ground. You can listen to Gilley if you want, or Banks. They argue between themselves. Why? because neither of 'em trusts the other and

125

they're both supposed to be Communists. Communism's all very well in theory but someone's got to run it, and then you've just swapped one bastard for another. Here life's no fun but at least we don't have to live in holes in the ground. Remember you're working for the Americans now and if you think all the cowboys are in the USA, think again. You're in Britain's biggest fuckin' rodeo.

"All you can do is forget it and try to keep your nose clean enough so no one knows it's dirty. They'll use you as a scapegoat if the smut on your nose shows too much, and they'll all hide behind your little bit of smut while they're pissing themselves 'cos they're sitting on bags of soot. Look after number one, kid, and if you can get one over on the bastards so much the better. That's why I always try to cut Gallatia up in the morning. One day I'll give the rancid little git a heart attack. You take it from me, kid, keep your head down and look after number one. Don't take sides; it's not worth it. Sell your soul to the Company and you're theirs for life, and you'll be an arsehole for life or crazy or dead, and the same goes for the union. Some of the stewards are all right but in the end the good ones are just whipping boys for the Company - useful for making examples of. Take it from me. Keep your head down. God don't rule here. It's the devil that rules and Henry Ford the Second's the devil."

43

Reorganisation

Monday January 11th 1965 8.00 a.m:

Outside the departmental office behind the canteen, miniature tornadoes carrying swirling grey coke dust snake up the road on a

126

vicious, dry ice, north-east wind. Inside, scuffed, light green walls, not with a dado, just a line at waist height where the colour changes to gradations of nicotine stained cream, culminating in a grey brown ceiling, tainted even worse by the smoke of a thousand cigarettes hanging in a stinking pall for years. The stuffy, centrally heated atmosphere is laden today, not just with smoke, but with intense disquiet. Eyes studiously not meeting eyes, repelled by faces, hypnotised by the dirty ceiling, walls and floor.

"Contact all the foremen and get them in here for nine o' clock." Gallatia, the general manager, is speaking tersely to Mrs Short, his secretary.

Nine o' clock and the foremen are gathered.

Gallatia pauses, his face the colour and texture of sandstone as he scans the room. Then to a silence bred from his look, he begins, "I've got you here to let you know that these accidents must stop. We've headed off some of the worst publicity, partly because it happened at the weekend and partly because BIC next door have had an accident involving an illegal immigrant who they've been accommodating on the premises."

Everyone knows what he's talking about but he doesn't speak of Fred at all. No expression of sadness, sorrow or regret. No mention of Fred's wife or children. He'd tear up Fred's clock card, erase his number and forget he ever existed, if he could. He did exist, though; I knew him; we weren't great friends but he was real. To treat him as though he was nothing just a number on a card, or a dust mote reflecting sunlight for a second, then whisked away on the wind, simply isn't right, it's unnatural, unhealthy, inhuman.

"This time we were lucky and next door took some flak otherwise headed for us. I've had instructions to make it clear to you all that this is not to happen again. How you organise your departments is your direct responsibility. My job is to delegate and ensure results. Recently production targets have not been met and this latest accident might be construed by an inquiry to be the result of incompetence. We're here this morning to discuss ways and means of improving the department's safety record, whilst maximising production efficiency. I expect your full co-operation in applying any measures proposed. Is that clear?"

Acquiescence is indicated by obsequious grunts and nods.

"Any questions before I explain to you the proposals that I've been working on over the weekend?" He's selling the idea he's a hero of labour to make Russians weep. He'd have people believe that managing Fords' blast furnace is woven into the very fabric of his body.

None of the foremen wants to draw attention to themselves by being the first to speak. The silence that greets his speech shatters like glass at the impersonality of his next words.

"The proposals are as follows. I want to maintain a basic bloc of fitters in the maintenance shop, but I want each area in the plant allocated its own maintenance crew. The raison d'etre behind these changes is this: each resident crew will be clearer about what their functions are, will better understand the machines they are dealing with, and will be directly responsible to the relevant foreman for reaching set production targets. In this way I expect to achieve two objectives, (a) Improved safety and (b) increased production.

"Any questions?"

What can they say to a death treated as a statistic? They stand... apparently attentive, po-faced, mute; still none wants to draw attention to themselves by being first to speak, because in truth none are content with the way the situation is being handled. Gallatia himself is, again, obliged to break the church service silence that is the response to this second speech.

"Right the rest of you can carry on, but expect some radical moves that will mean major changes for us all. Obviously I'll be expecting, not just your support in these matters, but one hundred percent commitment to the new measures.

"Thank You."

This is discussion Company style. It's over! As the foremen disperse, Gallatia asks "Fred what's your work load like today? Have

128

you got time to work out a chart for redistributing the men around the plant? I'd like to see you in my office." Oddly, although he's a company man through and through, Fred Wilkinson is the only foreman who isn't basically a 'yes man'. Gallatia uses him warily as a 'hatchet man'. Wilkinson takes perverse pride in being very unpopular.

"I can do it in a general sort of way but there aren't enough men to go around. You know we used to run a system like the one you're proposing but to economise on labour we decided to put them in a pool. That's why we built the new workshop."

"Yes, but I'm sure you can find ways and means by which we can use the men economically and cover all the plants."

"The only way that we can do that is by using some of the men to cover two plants. Spread them that thin and you're losing any advantage you've gained. You know the ructions that would cause because of the variations in the different plants. Do that and you know as well as I do that, likely as not, you'll have a strike on your hands." Gallatia adopts his sandstone mask as he quietly and slowly grinds out these words: "Fred you're a good man. You're the most effective foreman I've got. I want you to go with me on this and instead of being negative I want you to really try and see what you can come up with. There has to be something we can do without expanding the workforce".

"I'll see what I can do but I'm no magician. I haven't got a magic wand."

"Go away and think about it. Sleep on it and come back to me tomorrow morning with a plan."

***

"This is it - the best I can do George. You can try it, but don't blame me for the consequences," as he hands Gallatia a sheet containing his plan for reorganising labour distribution around the plant.

"Hmm, I like that. Use that apprentice, Ray, and Woods the

labourer, in the sinter plant."

"Yeh the boy's learning bad habits from that smart-Alec Bernie in the by-products. He can do the job all right, but he's learning all the tricks in the book from Bernie, with his bloody war pension. The boy's getting too big for his boots and it might teach him his place. We tried the gentle approach when we put him in the drawing office, but he said he couldn't stand being shut in all day. His report from the Trade School says it all: 'Can be insolent'. It might teach him something if we put him there with Woods. That way I could keep my eye on the pair of them. Woods has been around this place too long for his own good, and it might cramp his style a bit if we tied him down to a fixed spot."

44

Darts Match

Friday January 15th 1965 8.00 p.m:

The Black and White is a big scruffy pub in High Street in Old Dagenham Village, shabby mock Tudor outside, and dejected, scuffed panelled, Victorio art deco within. Ill matched furniture of indeterminate history adds odd homely charm to down at heel, nicotine orange, tattyness. Somehow a feeling of welcome is conveyed through the burnished copper bar top, open fires and business-like polished beer pumps.

Tonight is a big night. Tom Wyatt, who I play darts with at lunchtime in the furnace workshop, is going to play another top man from Southend. There's big money bet on the outcome. Parker, the wheeler-dealer cleaner from Fords is taking bets, with a couple of serious heavies at his shoulders. I'm here to see the result. I've got a

130

fiver bet on Tom. I played him once for a pound. He bet me he would beat me while he played with sharpened three-inch nails instead of darts. He won, and finished, saying with a sardonic laugh, "You know **you** could play with nails, and as long as they're sharp, and you get the spin right, it'd make hardly any difference to your game. The only real difference is that more fall out. I'll take the pound off you for telling you that." I respected him for that. He had his own quirky principles and retained his humanity, even though he was involved in a game with a seriously shady side. He was teaching me the lesson that bets made on the definition of a word or sharp, silly little trick are traps set for the foolish.

The match was set up on a purely unofficial basis but was still a big event to those involved in local pub culture. A referee from Southwark, south of the river, and therefore viewed as a foreigner, with no allegiance to either side, has been brought in for the occasion.

Standing next to me is Gilley, his expensive beer belly leading the way before him, his flushed face wearing its customary half smile. Eight o'clock; everybody's got their pint, and the atmosphere's building. Our heroes are warming up, taking alternate turns to throw, one dart each. The referee calls the rules.

"Best of eleven games of five-oh-one. No double to start, double or 'bull' to finish. Nearest the 'bull' starts. Okay everybody, ready." Tom, with the blank face of a professional poker player, throws first, just outside the twenty-five wire. Southend next; hmmm, he's just inside the wire. Looks as though he's pretty good. Oh well, it's only a fiver and Tom warned me a gamble's a gamble. He should know. It's rumoured he's got a hundred quid on the outcome. He obviously thinks he can win. By game five the tension's mounting; it's been game for game so far. It's Southend to start. Oh dear, oh dear, a hundred and forty. Good, but not good. Tom's throw, sixty, sixty, twenty - one hundred and forty: shouts from the crowd. Go on Tom. Southend, trying to look cool, throws – twenty then five – jeers from Toms' supporters. Southend pauses - the referee shouts.

"All-right gentlemen, quiet please."

More jeers. Southend throws his last dart, five. Tom's men erupt. This game is now critical. Tom's crowd are alight. Yells of encouragement are deafening. Tom's at the line again and there's silence as if he'd stepped on a switch. The drip, drip of a leaky tap echoing in the gents accentuates the quiet. First dart - treble nineteen, then twenty and twenty: ninety-seven scored – textbook. Still there's deadly quiet. Southend is really under pressure now, even the tobacco smoke hanging in the air seems rigid with tension. Forty-five scored. Is Southend's nerve broken? Tom again, face still blank, shutting out everything around him - dart one, just outside the double sixteen wire, second dart - double sixteen. Can he do it again? Yes! The big room shakes with the roar from Tom's crowd. When it's over Tom's supporters are jubilant. Tom, obviously pleased, standing on a chair and waving his arms for quiet, shouts,

"I'd like to thank the landlord for letting us use this place and letting you rowdy lot in. Second I'd like to thank the referee. Not a job I'd fancy; there's always someone moaning. Last of all on a more serious note I'm putting a tenner of my winnings in the whip round for Fred at work's missis. I'm told she'll get a year's wages and that's all and it'll probably be a year before she gets it. Banks is passing the hat round. You've all had a good night so hopefully you'll put something in to make Fred's missis' week a bit better. It's the least we can do."

Faces flushed with success or hangdog and aggrieved at their loss momentarily become solemn. Even the Southend men, on hearing what the collection is for, dutifully contribute, almost as though in church, and embarrassed into dropping something on the plate.

"Did you have any money on it Gilley?" I ask.

"Aye just a pound though, just for sociability's sake."

A loud voice exclaims; "Fucking gamesmanship; Willy was sabotaged by their yelling, and then they expect us to give any cash we've got left to a collection for one of their mates."

Gilley yells.

"If we had a government that looked after those who did the

132

producing, then there'd be no need for collections for the relatives of the dead.' (extra loud). "Fred's missis'll need more than a bunch of flowers from the local Labour Party."

From the back of the room someone calls, "Sounds like you want to fuck off to Russia."

Wyatt, already the worse for drink, stands on a table to yell great chunks of Shakespeare, half laughing in an attempt to defuse the situation (God knows where he learnt that). Jittery, unstable quiet drops like a butchers cleaver in sawdust as a new kind of expectant tension envelops the crowd.

"Aye. Well until the unions and the government are one we're puppets of the ruling class. Joe Stalin may have been a bastard but at least he was our bastard. The Labour Party in the end'll prove to be just another link in Marx's chains that bind the working classes."

Shit, I'm looking for space to back away from Gilley, there's going to be trouble, I can feel it. Gillie's big, but he's old; he must be crazy, he's courting trouble. There's no room to merge into the crush. Everybody seems to have the same idea, he's being shunned, like a man in a crummy ad for deodorant. Banks, to his credit, as a fellow Communist, is pushing to get closer to Gilley, leading with his shoebox full of cash. Brown follows Banks, shouting lamely.

"Who gave us the National Health Service?"
Gilley's got the bit between his teeth now and roars,

"That's just a sop to stop what the Labour Party" - his face distorted with derision as he speaks these words - "think is the rot coming from Russia." A resounding crash interrupts the argument, then a moment of silence and the landlady is seen standing on a stool behind the bar wielding a two foot long Indian club. She's a big woman. In a deep voice brimming with confidence she proclaims,

"You can use filthy language; you can bring tarts; you can get pissed; but anyone talking religion or politics in my pub'll have me to deal with." Glasses rattle as she brings the club down on the bar with a second bruising thump.

Gilley, eyes blazing, carries his great belly with steady dignity from the bar.

"That's it, fuck off back under the bed," calls one of Parker's heavies. The landlady, with an athleticism that belies her bulk, lifts the bar flap and is suddenly berating the offender, hitting him with the club just hard enough to make an impression, whilst yelling "Out! Out! Get out of my pub." Great, swaggering bully though he is, he sheepishly leaves in reverse, defending himself with his forearms from the rain of blows from the club.

An audible sigh of relief is heard throughout the bar. People laugh at the spectacle of the threatening bodyguard retreating before the onslaught of the landlady. Animated chatter resumes, with members of the crowd recounting their part in the events. The landlady, scary heroine of the hour, resumes pint-pulling, face blank, eyes shuttered, as dry mouths resort to extra pints. Tills ring, pockets empty, beating hearts slow, but like a ripple in a pool, murmured rumour spreads; the crowd, reanimated, moves out of the pub, a mob creature greater than its parts with a voyeuristic life of it's own.

A shout: "Call an ambulance. Someone's battered the old Scots bloke."

45

Playing the System

Monday January 18th 1965 8.20 a.m:

"Well, work your loaf, and it needn't be too bad. Some of the others won't like it. If you take it, you'll be doing a man's job whilst still an apprentice, so you can expect some stick for that, but no one else will want the job and you'll have Stan. We could try to get him made up to fitter. If we can get Rancy to push for that, it'll probably be okay. The sinter plant used to be quite reasonable till they brought in the pool system. That was a daft idea. Nobody gives a shit whether the plant works or not with the pool. If a machine breaks down, someone gets it going again. It doesn't matter how. If it breaks down again, two days later, it gets bodged again. As time goes on, the plant gets into a right state, and that's what's happened in the sinter plant. The first thing to do there is get the place cleaned up. If everything is covered in dust and grit then maintenance is bound to be more difficult. With all those broken windows letting in the grit from the coke-ovens, on top of the ore dust, the place is bound to be filthy. The first priority is to fix the windows."

This was the advice of Bernie. I've just learnt from Rance that I'm to be moved again and given the job of maintaining the sinter-plant. If the furnace is Siberia, the sinter plant is the far north.

I don't know what to think; this is real responsibility: three hundred and fifty feet of conveyor belt; three mixing hoppers; twenty five ordinary pumps and the two sludge pumps that pump cooling water to the great copper tuyeres (pronounced tweers), through which the hot blast is forced to the furnace. All this is to be my responsibility! The sludge pumps **have** to run night and day, or the furnace could be rendered useless. Add to this the sixty steel pallets on which the sinter is heated to a thousand degrees and the task looks daunting. On the plus side is the fact that I'll be running my own show, with the help of Stan, who is without doubt the best of the labourers and a person I get on with. Bernie has pointed out that the job can be good if tackled properly so, 'Yeh let's have a go.' If things go wrong I really have nothing to lose. If I wreck something 'So what!' They can only sack me. Nothing would make me happier.

"Bloody hell, we're supposed to work in this?" I look at Stan, my heart in my boots. The space is quite big with a dirty bench fitted with two heavy vices, running twenty feet along one wall. Along the walls at the sides are racks containing spare parts, mostly covered in dusty old black grease and looking as though they belong in the scrap bin. In the far corner is the lift, with stairs adjoining. The walls consist of bare iron girders clad on the outside with corrugated iron.

There are windows all around. All those not broken are coated with a film of the reddish brown greasy iron ore dust that lies over everything. It has collected in small drifts like fine red-brown snow where girders met floor. Everything is filthy. The major source of the muck is evident. A conveyor belt rattls with a rhythmic thump as its joints bump over rollers. Each thump scatters a little more dust to add to the reddish fog that fills the air. Operators move around, footsteps muffled by the dust, in a twilight of the damned, eyes, noses and lips outlined with a congealed coating of the filthy red muck.

The whole building vibrates night and day from the movement of the sinter pallets on the floors above as they carry their load of mixed ores under giant grill burners. This enormous oven makes hundreds of tons of glowing, permeable sinter cake daily, baked at a 1000 degrees C, and created to speed the melting process in the heart of the insatiable furnace. The whole structure is stamped with ugly industrial gloom, a scene-set from a gothic novel, brought to life.

It's winter so the whole place is just very warm. The steel plates of the floor ring underfoot and act as radiators, keeping the plant warm, despite the freezing weather outside. In summer the heat will be unbearable.

Stan laughs, "Don't worry, kid, you're looking at the best quartermaster's scavenger in the British Army. We can fix this place up a treat. They're putting a new line in at the tractor plant and there'll be some sectional office partitions going begging soon. With a few of them we can make a really nifty little cubbyhole. We're on the fourth floor so we can fit a warning system to let us know when anyone's coming. This is a chance to build our own little empire. Get this place sorted, kid, and it'll be the 'Life of Riley' up here."

So we 'set to,' beginning with seized rollers on the conveyor belts. First we brush away the dust so we can see what is happening. Ill lubricated, dust-seized rollers first wear a flat like a face on the side of a nut, and eventually wear through, creating an edge like a razor that will slice through the conveyor belt like a ham slicer at the butchers. Destruction can be total, often jamming the whole machine, creating hours of heavy work, simply to sort out the jam. We become adept at replacing rollers and work till all run freely. With the conveyors running more smoothly, the dust fog thins

✍✍✍✍

46

Strike

Tuesday February 2nd 1965 8.45 a.m:

"You're on strike."

"Ah... wh... What?"

"You're on fuckin' strike - Aren't you?" Tom Wyatt has two bunches of my overalls in his big workman's hands and he's lifting me from the floor, his eyes are bulging and his bared teeth are six inches from my face (I think he's probably annoyed about something). I can smell the tailor made cigarettes he smokes on his breath.

"Yeah, Tom I'm on strike," I say soothingly. How does it go, discretion is the better part of valour? Apprentices aren't supposed to strike, but I've no idea what's going on and Tom Wyatt is half as big as me again, so for the moment I'm on strike.

"Go and stand by the wall with the others then."

"What's going on Gilley? I walked through the door to go to the stores and Wyatt picked me up and told me I was on strike?" Gilley, sporting sutures above his partially closed left eye, still livid from Friday's attack, but wearing his customary grin replies,

"It seems the management have cut overtime. They usually do it when the car parks are full but they don't usually apply it to our department, because they know the furnace has to keep going or it's finished for good. My guess is they've dropped a bollock and applied it to us too, in error. Ah believe there's some question about you too.

137

They're saying you're doing a man's work and you're an apprentice. You're working with a labourer and there has to be the question of who's in charge. Is it you or is it him? Either way there's some changes to be made. Either they make him up to fitter and he's in charge or they shorten your apprenticeship and make you up.' Throughout this speech his face is cracked with a grin and he appears to be on the verge of bursting with laughter, oddly out of place on his battered face. He seems to find the whole situation hilarious. It does seem daft - there are probably forty of us all lined up along the wall of the main workshop wondering what to do. We're milling about a bit but generally staying by the wall. In the office are six foremen talking animatedly. They appear to be as confused as I am. I get the feeling that no one really knows what's going on and this, I guess, is what Gilley finds so funny. This place is such a shambles.

Fred Wilkinson and Banks, the shop steward, have appeared from the main offices and are speaking to the foremen in the maintenance workshop office. Us by the wall stop milling around, expectant, waiting for something to happen, feeling awkward, wanting some resolution.

Wilkinson followed by Banks, George Brown and the rest of the foremen line up before us in the main workshop. We stand tense, with our backs to the wall. A comedian calls, "It's the magnificent seven," while another mournful voice is heard singing to the tune of the Internationale:

"The working class can kiss my arse,
I've got the foreman's job at last."

There's a murmur of laughter and some of the tenseness is relieved as the jokes highlight the craziness of the situation.

"All right. All right. That's enough."

Wilkinson, with true managerial flair, has confidently taken charge at exactly the right moment and the strikers patiently listen.

"The information that was received earlier from the main office was issued by mistake. Overtime will continue to be available to those who want it on the usual terms. In return the company will expect, as has been established by customary practice, that you men will work a least two hours a week overtime when required. Banks here has agreed that that is acceptable. The company has apologised for any misunderstanding that has been caused and hopes that we can amicably return to the status quo. Off the record, I can assure you all that heads will roll in the main office over this fiasco."

"There is one other question I may as well deal with now. During our conversation this morning Mr Banks pointed out to me that there has been some concern among you that Ray there," fixing me with a baleful look, "has been working with Woods on the maintenance of the sinter plant despite the fact that he has not finished his apprenticeship. The company has agreed that this state of affairs has come about due to the recent reorganisation and represents a technical oversight on the part of the company. We have consequently agreed that Mr Woods will now be recognised as a qualified fitter."

Wilkinson has handled things beautifully. The situation has been stabilised without any loss of face on either side. The men feel they have won a small victory, gaining Stan's promotion. Stan will now be paid a little extra money in recognition of his improved status, though the amount is so small as to be insignificant. This move on the part of the management has overcome some of the discontent still felt among the employees over the railway line affair. There is also some smugness among the men in the furnace department that although the main factory people face the overtime cut, they don't.

All these men tend to live beyond their means and can't survive without overtime, so to cut overtime almost inevitably causes a strike because, as the men see it, they are forced to do overtime when it suits the company; therefore, on a tit for tat basis, they think the company must provide them with the overtime they need to meet their commitments. This invariably gives the company the whip hand because there are times when it suits them to lay men off. In this situation they simply cut overtime and the men in a knee jerk reaction go on strike. The end result is that the company gains because if they laid men off they would be obliged to pay a proportion of wages.

The strike in the main plant allowed the company to install a new production line and move the medical department, without disrupting production. At the same time sales weren't meeting expectations, so the company needed a layoff anyway. A strike at that moment provided the company with a double benefit. The union reps' seem unaware of this. Are they naïve? Are they stupid? Are they in the management's pocket?

"What's going on Gilley? This is daft."

"We've a meeting upstairs in the Black and White at half seven on Wednesday next week. If you come to that you'll begin to understand how this place works. It's not simple; it takes time to get to grips who's doing what and why, especially when there's no logic to what some people do."

47

Foundations of an Empire

Monday February 8th 1965 8.00 a.m.
Stan's now a qualified fitter. I'm pleased for him, and even more pleased that the resentment that some of the men have expressed towards me, as being some sort of scab, has been overcome with Stan's promotion.

Frank Rance is happier too, because some of the men held him responsible for the situation where I was working as a qualified man, when still an apprentice. His mood as he does his rounds in the mornings, to check how things are going, is more genial, and he gives us no trouble because we are clearly making inroads into getting the place sorted out.

We've asked for glass to replace the broken windows. He baulks at first but we explain to him that there are two reasons behind the request. Firstly, it will reduce the need for internal lighting, because we will be able to clean all the windows inside and out (We've learnt that the fire brigade used to use our building for hose practice whilst also cleaning the windows) and secondly, it will enable us to keep the place cleaner. Better cleanliness equals less maintenance and greater safety. Having armed him with an explanation to convince management, he goes away happy.

A labourer is allocated to spend some time sweeping throughout our building. I don't know how Stan coaxed him into spending more time with us, and don't ask. Stan was the middleweight boxing champion of the army and as such isn't someone to argue with lightly. Despite his receding greying hair, he still has the air of a man to be reckoned with. He's got a lower jaw like the bottom half of an upright piano, that underlines a grin to give foremen nightmares. His dancing eyes smile with calm assurance in his ability to complete any task he sets out to tackle. Somehow I find myself doing things he wants without even realising he's influenced me. He's 'cool'. If things get tough I feel he'll be tough enough to meet the situation.

I'm begining to feel my feet. Between us Stan and I have managed to build an 'office' that's reasonably clean, where we can sit in relative comfort. As we make inroads into the regular maintenance and start to get the machines into reasonable order, our workload is being reduced. We are no longer 'fire fighting' simply to keep the plant running. We're beginning to be able to plan.

The biggest single problem on the job is the sludge pumps. These account for nearly a day in a week of our time. One has to run constantly; if it fails, then the standby must be ready to take its place. They cool the furnace tuyeres. (The nozzles through which hot air is forced into the furnace). If they stop, the three hundred and fifty feet tall furnace could be wrecked. As a consequence, neither has been properly maintained because no one has had the courage to strip one and deny the cover of a spare. Both are 'knackered'.

They work in much the same way as bellows. Eccentric bearings on shafts operate diaphragms, but the bearings are so worn that the shafts hammer into the diaphragms, giving them such a beating they seldom last longer than a week. I hate being responsible for machines in such a poor state. It reflects on me as a person that they are not properly looked after. The noise they make sets my teeth on edge, my stomach tightening in apprehension that the inevitable bang will come, indicating damage beyond repair. I feel like a gardener watching plants die for lack of care. I'm resolved to replace the faulty bearings and fix the problem. This means a complete rebuild that might take two or three days for each pump but 'what the hell.' We stand to gain almost a day a week if we can sort the pumps out and if the two break down together then it'll be us who carry the can.

I've settled down to carefully prepare a list of all the parts needed.

"What are you plotting?" Stan asks, as I pore over the grubby old pump parts list.

"I'm getting ambitious. We're going to fix those sludge pumps for good."

"They'll never give you any fuckin' dynamite."

"We won't need it. I've been ordering the bits in dribs and drabs so no one noticed what I'm doing. All we've got to do now is go to the stores and get the parts before anyone realises what we're up to."

"Huh I wondered if you'd get around to it. You'll have Rancy jumping better than if you tickled his balls."

"I'm sure we can do it. How long do you think it'll take? I think we should be able to do it in two days. Are you game for a bit of overtime?"

"You know me kid, always welcome a bit of extra cash. Might even get into double time on that job if we can get Rancy in enough of a panic. I've never seen him crap himself yet. Spread those bits around the floor enough and you just might get him shitting his pants," he said with a malicious laugh.

We worked to get everything running as well as we could, as I

142

gradually phoned orders through to the stores for all the new parts we needed.

Monday and we're ready to start the job . Dead on time we switch to the better of the two pumps. All the tools we need are at hand. We begin the strip down. By nine thirty there's no going back. The main bearing is next to dismantle.

"What the fuck do you think you're playing at? If the other pump stops we're right in the shit," Rance is yelling at me. I'm ready. I've anticipated his reaction.

"Eventually both these pumps were going down together. If one of the frames cracked then we truly would have been 'in the shit' and these bearings are so knackered it was on the cards - that could have happened anytime, then who'd have carried the can? The job's going fine. The best thing you can do is leave us alone to get on with it. The less interference we get, the sooner the job will be done. If you really want to help, send Bernie from the by-products down here. That's the only way you're going to speed things up."

"If the other pump packs up you're sacked". With those words he went. "Short, even if it wasn't sweet," laughs Stan. "I wonder if he's going to the bog?"

We work all day with just a couple of stops for food. Rance comes back a couple of times for a rant but we plod on steadily. By eight o clock in the evening we've replaced the main bearing. After testing the fit I say, "Shit, Stan, I can't leave it this tight or it'll seize up. It's got to come off again."

"Yeh, you're right, but it's only a bit and we're doing really well. It'd be ready to run in a couple of hours at the rate we're going and that'd only be two hours double time. If we can go past midnight we're on triple time. I've only had triple time on bank holidays before so it's **got** to come to bits again." I'm still laughing when Rance turns up, looking pointedly at his watch. "What do you think you're pissing about at, standing around and treating the business as a joke when the job's critical? Get on with it and fuckin' stop messing about."

"Naughty, naughty Frank. No need for rudeness. That's no

way to talk to Dave, a young apprentice, when he's sorting out your job for you," Stan said, parading his most insolent grin. "We were thinking of going home and if you insist on being rude we'll have to. Be nice and we might stay and finish the job."

"You'd bloody well better or you're in deep shit. I'll see to it. I want this job finished tonight. Tonight." He is begging, almost hysterical. "We can do it but we might not be finished till the morning." I say.

"I don't care how fuckin' long it takes, I want it finished," he almost screams, eyes bulging and face scarlet as he stomps off, shaking his head. Part of me feels sorry for him. He's worried half to death. I think he really might have a heart attack or something.

"Ha ha - triple time here we come." Stan isn't bothered.

At eleven forty five the job is done. After a final oiling, I ask, "Who's going to press the button?"

"Take it steady kid we're still not on treble time yet. Oh go on then, start the fucking thing." I press the button.

"Fuckin' 'ell kid – sweet as treacle. Sounds like a different machine. Calls for a celebration. I'll go and make the tea."

The pump is running so sweetly it'll carry on for a month without stopping and instead of the gut wrenching bang, bang, bang, the noise it makes is whissssh-whooosh, whissssh- whooosh. Now it's back running so well even Rance will have no option but to congratulate us. We've fixed it between us - Stan will clock us both out at two o clock in the morning and I'll clock us back in at eight. It's not long after midnight and I'm home but I reckon we've earned some treble time.

***

Who the hell is running this job? I'm supposed to be an apprentice. They're supposed to be showing me how it's done, and I'm 'taking the piss' out of foremen. What is going on?

True, it was with the help of Stan, but I organised that job and

144

it couldn't have gone better. Add to that the fact that we were sorting out the hours we worked by manipulating the foreman. This had to be crazy.

I worked out the hours: fifty-one and two thirds if I do no more overtime in the week. I felt as though I'd been on the booze for a weekend but I'd earned more money today than anyone else in the plant apart from Stan and perhaps Parker, even as an apprentice. Things were getting weird, out of kilter, unbalanced.

The world isn't supposed to be like this. I'm supposed to be the boy learning the job. Instead I'm running the job and making a success of it. A not particularly bright kid from a council estate was showing trained adults how the job should be done by the simple application of common sense. It was good for my ego but rather than getting puffed up, I was shocked. It was a revelation that the bosses were just ordinary people, like me, apparently not as good as me at doing the work they'd spent a lifetime training for. Why? Clearly they weren't stupid - so why, why, why?

Frank Rance didn't do what he thought was rational. He did what he did for other reasons. What were the reasons? Why? Company men were attempting to stop me achieving objectives that were clearly to the advantage of the company. Why? I didn't formulate these ideas as clearly as this at the time, but I knew in my gut that the way the company worked was not as simple as outward appearances indicated. I was operating with a set of values that I'd assumed were universal. I was brought up to tell the truth and I expected other people to do the same. That pump gave me the beginning of a lesson it took a lifetime to learn. I was just starting to get the ghost of a grasp on the truth.

I'd already begun to think about exactly what truth is, and concluded it's different for everyone. I knew that when I saw a bolt it was something entirely different to what my sister saw. For her it was something associated with dirt, mechanical things, engines and machines that didn't concern girls - until they went wrong, then they were frustrating things that were just a nuisance and a bother.

145

I saw a circular wedge that as you tighten stretches like rubber and so locks itself in position. Bolts were masterpieces of design that had a stark beauty and elegance as well as being solidly functional. To get the best from them you needed a 'feel' that had something to do with art. My truth had to do with art and emotion, but the truth of those who ran the Company was simple, crude, and tied to hard cash and plain numbers on a balance sheet of cash and power

48

Stan and Me and the life of Riley

The sludge pump proved to be a watershed in the relationship between Rance and me, or perhaps I should say between Stan and me, as a kind of faction, and Rance acting as a buffer between the management and us. Rance was in an impossible position. He'd disapproved of our action and yet was delighted with the result. Quite how he explained what had happened to Galatia is difficult to know but the upshot was that from then on he pretty well left us to get on with it. His visits became more sporadic and as we steadily cleaned up the job he simply grunted his approval and went off to do more important things.

Stan and I fixed the other pump and our workload was reduced enormously. Now we could take it easy all week or doss around and do virtually nothing for at least a day a week. The plant ran more smoothly and production targets were met with ease.

***

With the arrival of spring, the plant was getting hotter. Stan and I were gossiping one morning and the question of our workshop came up.

"You know I went into the main factory yesterday. You'll never guess what I saw," said Stan.

"Don't tell me. The Queen mother was passing round the gin wearing an Ascot hat like an umbrella to catch the pigeon shit."

"Huh. No, the scrappers were ripping down the medical to make room for the new line, and do you know what's in the medical?"

"Don't tell me one of those animals has got his hands on that juicy new nurse."

"Forget about what's in your trousers for two minutes and listen. They're taking out a whole air conditioning system. It's got filters, washers, it's the whole business. We could fit it here and make this the most comfortable office in the plant."

"Why didn't you tell me? Lets go and have a look." We didn't slink; we were brazen. I wore my apprentice's white coat and, based on the old army adage carried a drawing - 'Walk around carrying a clipboard, looking important, and you'll have nothing else to do all day'. In a factory with a day shift of seventeen thousand employees, believe me, it works.

We reached the site of the old medical department without incident. The structure that had housed three full time nurses and where Ted's hand had been patched up six months ago, before they took him to hospital, was gone. This building within a building, that three days before had provided medical cover for thousands of employees, was no more. In its place was a great open space, over a hundred yards long, where the only evidence of its existence was a series of equispaced holes and a patch of relatively clean plastic tiles among a sea of greasy wood-blocks that made up the floor of the rest of the factory.

"Fuck it, Stan. Why didn't you tell me before?"

"Don't panic. You boys are just like the foremen, rush, rush, rush, Oh, missed the chance; the scrappers have been primed, just

147

keep walking and look casual." We coolly strolled past the main control room while six foremen watched, then out of the main entrance to the turnstiles at the main gate where dozens of stillages lay full of scrap taken from the cleared part of the factory. Quite what the deal was I had no idea, but after a few words with a person sitting in a lorry parked by the scrap, Stan walked over to me and pointing, said.

"What do you think? Can we do anything with that lot?" In the stillage was not one air conditioning unit but two; in another stillage beside was a third, plus the adjustable bed and a couple of quality chrome chairs that two days previously had graced the waiting room of the medical department. The whole lot was virtually new.

"Will we get away with it?"

"It's scrap, who's going to bother? He's happy," said Stan, nodding and directing his eyes towards the scrap man.

"How will we get it around to our place?" We'd walked nearly half a mile through the factory and this lot would have to come by road.

"Not a problem. Leave it to me. All I need to know is, can we get it to work?"

"The manufacturer's instructions would make it easier, but it shouldn't be too difficult as long as the scrap men haven't wrecked the bloody things."

"Right, you stroll back and I'll see to it. It'd probably be better if you went by the road." I went back to the sinter plant and started getting tools ready to fix a gearbox which was causing problems on one of the sinter mixers. Stan arrived, rolled up the shutter door, and calmly drove in a fork truck loaded with one of the stillages. Having dropped his load, he reversed out yelling, "Shut the door for me."

An hour later he was back to drop the second stillage. Goodness knows where he got the fork truck. When he finally came back it was lunchtime. I wandered over to see Bernie. It was spring. The sunshine filled me with pleasure, even with its backdrop of grey industrial buildings. An odd lone daffodil, which against overwhelming odds was flowering by the polluted pastel-green stream running alongside the factory fence, made me feel there was hope for the world, even in the dismal place where men had created such ugliness.

Bernie, who, learning of our new acquisition, was keen to visit, walked back with me.

"Stanley, you crafty bastard. How did you swing it with the scrap man?"

"'Bernie, you know there's always a way. In this case it was Parker. Not the sort of bloke you'd normally want to deal with, but I had leverage. He's the proud owner of the third unit."

"Ah ... Got it, the third unit financed the other two?"

"Plain and simple's always best."

As a callow youth of twenty I wasn't sure what was going on, but at the mention of Parker I gained a glimmer of understanding. Parker was a legend. Inside the factory he ran his business that had a far greater turnover than many good sized legitimate businesses on the outside. He supplied anything to order, if you were prepared to wait. You could have a bet or buy anything from cigarettes and condoms to a new car, even down to the colour required, and always at a massive discount. Quite how it was done none but Parker knew. There were those who thought Parker's activities might not be entirely legal. He ran the business from a broom cupboard, protected by a selection of massive padlocks. That cupboard was a treasure-trove. Ridiculous as it sounds, his job ostensibly consisted of sweeping up. This was ideal for someone who needed to move around in the factory. With his barrow festooned with brushes and shovels he was able to deliver goods to his regulars. He indirectly supplied several local tobacconists' shops on a regular basis, and at Christmas he did a roaring trade, in booze. When a lorry was hijacked on the main road by the factory, huge quantities of cheap spirits were always available.

49

Parker and a Hall of Mirrors

Parker was just the clear evidence of the subculture that existed within the factory. During the day he wandered around in filthy overalls, looking every inch a "cleansing operator'. His dark, jowly, sullen face was known everywhere. He knew everyone, but trusted no-one. His eyes were seldom still, he had the restlessness of both hunter and hunted. His day started when he arrived in a top of the range car, fancier than Gallatia's. He carried a brief case. It probably contained his lunch, though he must have kept some sort of accounts. He almost managed to look the smart executive, but his clothes were too flashy and expensive. On his wrist hung a heavy gold bracelet, while at his neck swung a gold sovereign medallion.

***

Everything got crazier and crazier. No wonder more than one in ten of the foremen cracked up. I wanted to know what the company was. When I started, I thought its aims were clear: to make things and to make a profit, but I'd learnt it wasn't that simple. It was much more complicated than that. Gallatia was the manager and at one level he did just that, but at another level he did something else. Strikes which were supposed to be a blight on industry were being fomented by the management in one department, though not another - a sure way to lower the morale that management **said** was so important.

Gallatia knew Parker was covertly running a business inside the factory - everybody knew. Why was he allowed to carry on? There were wheels within wheels. Nothing was simple. The place was as crazy as Alice in Wonderland. It was a hall of mirrors. A Russian doll, always there was another inside. How was that? Why?

I was only half aware of all these questions but still I looked for answers. Until this time I'd read *Biggles*, engineering and bike magazines and the *Daily Mirror*. I'd read things like *Adam Bede* and *Tess of the D'Urbervilles* but I'd read them simply as novels, not social history. *The Ragged Trousered Pilanthropists* had begun to open my eyes. Now, browsing in the local library, probably at the suggestion of Gilley, I picked up a copy of *Germinal*. I couldn't put it down. It pointed out the injustice of the system, the apathy and even support for the oppressors of working people by those very working people.

There was something though, some point that it missed. I was left elated, but in the back of my mind was a niggling doubt that something wasn't right.

***

The air conditioners were state of the art. I doubted if there was anything as sophisticated as this in the main office, and they had a helicopter pad on the roof. Well, maybe, on second thoughts... Still - Gallatia had nothing like them in his office, but we needed them. It was getting hotter and hotter up there and we needed something to stop the dust. Old Tom the greaser had emphysema so bad he could hardly walk ten yards without stopping, and the lagger wasn't much better. Old Joe, Fred the dead rigger's mate, breathed like a steam engine as well, and it was likely as not something to do with the dust in the bloody place. Shit... Fred... I wondered what was happening about that?

It kept happening. I could see his face, his eyes caved into the sockets, and lips blue, then it turned into his hand disappearing, and me. Was it my fault? I knew it wasn't, but it might have been partly me. If I'd just held on a bit longer, but I'd have gone with him and it wouldn't have been the water, just thirty feet into the hopper. What would I have looked like then? What...? Head bashed in and blood all over the place or another 'lucky' statistic on the safety shield. Broken arm, leg, back, a basket case, slobbering down my front and in

151

nappies. It didn't bear thinking about; I shivered at the thought, I'd rather be dead. How would mum have felt?

***

I was wary of fitting the air conditioning system in our workshop, but having talked to Stan about it and having got the thing, there was little else I could do, so off we went 'in for a penny'. We set to with a will. Within two days it was up and running and a marvellous success. Our 'office' was transformed into one of the most comfortable places in the factory. The air was clean for the first time ever and we could adjust the temperature to any level we liked, warm in winter but more important cool in summer. Stan insisted on fitting an extra door to create an air lock and cut up old conveyor belts to cover the floor. After being used to bare steel plates, the whole atmosphere was changed. It was almost better than home. There was always the vibration from the sinter conveyor passing through the frame of the building but that was quite relaxing, like the hum from the engines of a big ship. Now walking around on the thick rubber of the conveyor belt, with its absorbent firm resilience underfoot, it had many of the attributes of the most luxurious, sound deadening carpet. We white-washed the inside of most of the windows, leaving the odd peephole so we could keep a check on the movements of foremen, and put up posters to brighten the place up. We'd created a clean fresh space that was all our own. As Stan had said. we were close to leading 'The Life of Riley.'

Word soon got around and we had a constant stream of visitors from around the department. Reactions ranged from the envious to those who laughed. Comments varied from "brilliant," to "You'll never get away with it." Rance called and was clearly astonished at the transformation of our filthy workshop. He opened the new door, and turned around twice, wide-eyed. His mouth opened and closed twice. I think he was too stunned to speak, then he said, "Gallatia won't like this" and walked out. For weeks nothing changed and we

152

began to relax and enjoy our newfound popularity. Stan continued to live up to his promise of being the best quartermaster's scavenger in the British army by providing a small electric cooker, so we could have heated food; and on Sundays, we even started charging for breakfasts whilst earning double time. We installed a pressure switch under a loosened stair, that rang a bell warning us of the arrival of visitors, and the lift was already fitted with a light showing it was in operation, so we always had time to prepare for unexpected visits from the management.

I set about organizing a preventive maintenance programme to plan ahead and make the best use of our time and reduce breakdowns, while beginning to create a stock-pile of regularly required spares, reducing our need to visit the stores. The time we spent actually repairing machines continued to decline, and our lives steadily became easier. We even had time to sleep on the comfortable bed from the old medical room. Life was good, and getting better all the time.

50

Big Ideas

I'd decided to reveal to Stan an idea I'd had floating in my head for some time.

"I've got this idea, Stan. What's the biggest job we've got left?"

"Bearings on the sinter pallets."

"How many bearings do you think we replace in an average week?"

"Eight to a pallet, two pallets a week; sixteen."

"How much is one of those bearings, d'you think?"

"Go on, tell me."

"If I buy them in a shop, they're sixteen pounds each."

"Fuckin 'ell. More than half a week's wages. That dear?"

"Yeah, that dear. Guess how much that comes to over fifty weeks of the year?"

"A fucking sight more than my wages."

"You said it. It comes to twelve thousand eight hundred pounds. Nice little pools win, eh?"

"Fuckin' right."

"What I've got in mind is this. The last time I put in a suggestion Rancy and Smith, the thieving bastards, rejected it, rewrote it, and shared the proceeds. This time I'm going to get paid for it, and it's a winner. I'll need your help, but it's a maximum, how d'you fancy two hundred and fifty quid?"

"Two hundred and fifty quid is all very fine, but what is this wonderful suggestion?"

"What I want to do is fit an automatic greaser to grease the pallet bearings as they come past, then instead of getting squirted once a week, if they're lucky, by old Tom, they get a squirt every ten minutes or so. The bearing life should be doubled at least. It'll mean a load more grease and shit everywhere but the bearings'll last miles longer. What do you think?"

"Yeah, well, it sounds good, but what about the greasing machine?"

"Well, being aware of your amazing skills as a scrounger, I thought you might be able to see your scrap-man friend."

"Hmmm, might be able to do something, I suppose. I'll have a think about it. While we're talking about ideas, I've got an idea as well. Do you fancy working a weekend with a bit of something extra on the side?"

"What do you mean?'

"I want to tidy my car up before I sell it and I could do with some help. How about it?"

"I don't mind helping, but what do you want me to do? Surely it won't take a whole weekend to tidy your car?"

"Yeah. Well, what I've got in mind goes a bit beyond basic tidying. I've had a chat with the blokes who are doing the road by the main gate and they've said I can borrow their hut for a weekend. And what I thought was, we might take a wall down and get the car in there, it's plenty big enough and I can get a little gantry and then we'd be all set to do the work."

"What work? What do you mean?"

"I've got this mate on the engine line and he reckons he can fix me up with an engine and gearbox. I've already got a set of wheels and tyres, I can get a back axle; and I've got a new battery too. If you want, you can come in at the weekend and help me fit it all. We could do it on overtime and there'd be something in it for you 'cos I'd be able to sell the old car for more than I'd have to pay the Company for the new one. What do you think?"

At that moment the stair bell rang. Through the angled mirror above the stairs we could see flashes of white coat. "Foremen" whispered Stan. We rose from out seats and quickly set about looking busy. The door opened. It was Gallatia.

51

Gallatia

"Uh huh-Hmmm. Quite something."

"Frank tells me you did all this between you without any help at all. Is that so?"

"Yes."

"I see. Did you ask anyone's permission?"

"Er. No."

"Don't you think you should have?"

"To be quite honest, it just sort of grew."

"And did you have much to do with this growing?"

"Er, well yes."

"Hmm are you proud of yourself?"

"I'd not really thought of it like that, but I suppose so."

I wasn't used to this sort of conversation so I had no idea where it was leading though obviously it was not good. I was as non-committal as I could manage.

"You cut a hole in the wall to accommodate the air conditioner?"

"Yes."

"It could be said you damaged the building doing that."

"I suppose so," I said doubtfully.

"Hmm... Am I to take it you don't really think so?"

"You can't make an omelette without breaking eggs."

"Are you being cheeky lad?"

"No."

"What are you telling me, did you damage the building or not?"

"I think any damage done to the building is offset by what we've added to it."

"Are you arguing with me, boy?"

"No."

"Do you talk to your father like this?"

'Yes."

'Do you think your father knows better than you?"

'Some of the time, but not all the time."

'Where did that air conditioner come from?"

He was really after me now. "I asked one of the scrap-men if he minded me taking it. He said it was okay. We needed something to sort out the dust, and I thought it would be a good idea."

"Oh you did, did you. Well I'll let it go this time but watch you're step boy. I'm watching you." With that he left, followed by his retinue of foremen Smith and Rance, who as he turned looked daggers at me.

"Fuckin 'ell, kid, it looks like we've cracked it. He may not be crazy about it but in effect you've got his approval. If we keep our noses clean and heads down for a bit we're home and dry." This is Stan at his most optimistic.

"I don't know, Stan. I don't think you can trust them from one minute to the next. I don't think they even know what they want themselves... By the way, when did you have in mind this rebuild for your car?"

"That's it, you've got the idea now. It'll be like new when it's done. The best would be the weekend after next. Rancey's daughter's getting married and some of the other foremen are going to the wedding. I know for a fact that Smith's not, so it'll be him in for the weekend, so we can easily bullshit him about what we're doing. We could leave some bits of the spare sludge pump lying around to make it look as though we're doing something. What do you think?"

"Yeh, go on then, be a bit of a laugh, and get one over on the Company."

***

I started keeping a careful record of all the bearings we replaced on the sinter pallets. If Stan were able to get a greasing machine, then the likelihood was, that, providing I could get the idea to work, our

157

workload would again be drastically cut. The biggest single job we had left was replacing the bearings in the sinter pallet wheels. The environment that these worked in was so hostile that sometimes their life might be as short as six weeks, though my survey showed that the average life was around five months. In terms of cost to the company, this was tremendous. At about two hundred and fifty pounds a pallet (a particularly awkward one might take as long as two days to fix), plus the time of two men, maintenance of the pallets was extremely expensive and there were sixty of them. Our wages at the time were about twenty-five pounds a week, so each pallet cost about three hundred pounds each time it was given a basic overhaul. Prolong the life of a pallet by one hundred percent and the saving to the company would be approximately three hundred pounds a week or fifteen thousand a year. The maximum payout for a suggestion was five hundred pounds and this only applied if the suggestion saved five thousand pounds within one year. If Stan got hold of a greasing machine, and **if** we were able to get it to supply grease to the wheels in a satisfactory fashion, then our reward would be considerable. All told, a lot of ifs, but certainly worth a gamble.

We continued carrying out the regular maintenance work. We played crib, chess and darts in our new-found spare time and did odd jobs for home. I had time to do some reading and still the job improved. I introduced a fine water spray onto the mixed sinter as it went by conveyor to the top floor. This drastically cut the amount of dust created and coincidently rendered the cake produced more permeable, making the whole plant more effective, almost by mistake. Production targets continued to be surpassed, despite the fact that the hours we worked were cut. I was growing over confident and beginning to feel I could do no wrong.

For a hobby I started to mechanic for another apprentice who raced in something called moto-cross. I made a jig for manufacturing a 'bunch of bananas' racing exhaust system for his Austin Mini car. Mum's brother had a contract for stove-enamelling telephone parts, and he enamelled the finished job for me. When other racers saw the result they all wanted them. I made one or two more to sell and made a good profit but that didn't please 'Smiffy,' whose pit work I did, but I stashed away the jig as a potential source of cash.

ཤ཈ཤ཈

52

A Suggestion

Stan disappeared for hours on end. He went 'out and about' as he put it. He knew people all over the factory. One day he walked in saying with a grin,

"You've got your greaser. I can go and pick it up tomorrow, but we need to get hold of a fork truck.'

"You're a genius, Stan. You won't be sorry. I'll get it to work if it kills me."

"Make sure you get the suggestion in before you peg it, won't you."

"Thanks."

Getting unofficial use of a fork truck wasn't easy but we slipped an old condemned machine out of the back of the main stores at lunch-time, while no one was around, and with Stan driving, just managing to overcome the leaky hydraulics and slack steering, and me perched, giggling with nervous excitement beside him, made our latest collection at the scrap bins by the main gate. An hour later a quarter of a ton of automatic greasing machine lay in the middle of our workshop.

"Not the best, is it Stan?"

"You boys are all the same. Want fucking blood."

It was old and filthy but the scrap man insisted it was working when removed from the plant so we began stripping it. When cleaned and

159

rebuilt, it proved to be in quite good condition. It had, after all, been well lubricated, unlike so many of the machines we worked on.

"Now all we have to do is fit the bloody thing, Stan."

"You'd better bloody well make it work or you're in trouble with me as well as Rancey," said Stan, only half joking.

"Don't worry, it'll work." I said, not feeling quite as confident as I made out.

The pallets were about eight feet long, nearly a foot deep, and two feet wide, each weighing nearly a ton. On each corner were fitted the offending wheels. Shaped like railway wheels with a lip on the edge, they were about six inches in diameter, running on ordinary railtracks. Huge sprockets similar to those on a bike drove the pallets. In fact the whole thing ran like an enormous bike chain. Protruding from the centre of each wheel was a grease nipple.

Our task was to find a means of getting the grease nipple and connector of the greasing machine to interlock for just sufficient time for some grease to be injected. I'd thought about how this could be done and had come up with an idea that I thought was simple and elegant. I shaped a piece of metal with a tapered slot at either end that guided itself onto the grease nipple. The nipple hit the end of the slot, which was forced to spin against the weight of a spring and as it turned, hit a switch, causing the greaser to pump.

***

The weekend came when I'd agreed to work on Stan's car. He told me exactly what to do. Between us in ten minutes we had one wall of the contractor's hut laid on the ground. He'd got sheets of four by two to lay over the wall and he drove his car straight into the hut. In a quarter of an hour it was all over. His car was locked in the hut. The business was organised like a military operation. He'd borrowed a small crane and by Saturday afternoon we had the new engine in and running okay. Down came the wall of the hut and out he drove. It was all very risky but it was Stan who was taking the biggest chance. We got away with it okay. I think Stan must have been part Irish, he was so lucky. On Sunday, out came the wall again and in went the car.

"How did it go?" I asked

"It was fine. I went slowly till I got pretty well away from the main gate then put the running-in sign in the window and took it steady and it went a treat. All we've got to do now is fit the back axle."

With two of us working, it didn't take long. Cars were simpler in those days, and by lunch time we'd finished. That weekend we'd stolen an engine and gearbox, a back axle and a battery from the Company, whilst being paid time and a third on the Saturday and double time till Sunday lunch for fitting it. In a way I didn't feel good about it, but at the same time I relished the irony of it. By the end of the following week Stan had sold his car and replaced it with a new one from the Company at a discount. He came out at the end of the deal with a small profit and a new car, as well as being paid overtime for doing the work.

On Monday it was back to work on the pallet greaser. Getting that to work properly was much more difficult than fitting the stolen parts to Stan's car. Getting the thing to locate on the nipples took hours of patient experiment, but we got there in the end. Seeing the connector rolling over and over and knowing that each time it rolled it was supplying a squirt of grease, lessening our workload on the dirtiest job in our plant, was as satisfying a physical job as I've ever done.

"Fucking done it, Stan," I said triumphantly. "I told you we could. Now all there is to do is wait and see what difference it makes to the bearings. It's just a case of keeping your fingers crossed."

I spent time over the next four months carefully recording the life of each bearing. At the end of that time no new bearings were needed. The greasing machine had more than proved its worth. Now I entered the suggestion with chapter and verse written proof that it worked.

"We've got 'em by the bollocks, Stan. They can't avoid giving us our cash now." How wrong I was.

53

Pride comes Before a Fall

Our workload was cut again. No pallets to fix equalled more time to doss around. Now if we had two days work a week we began to think we were hard done by. Our wages were reaching the money for old rope stage. Two days after submitting the suggestion, the phone rang.

"Is that Ray, the apprentice?"

I recognized the voice. Gallatia.

"Yes Mr Gallatia, that's me.'

"I want to see you in my office in ten minutes."

"Right, I'll be there."

I walked at a sharp pace to his office, so I was early. He signalled through the glass door that he knew I was there and I should wait. There was no seat. Five minutes passed, then ten. I was clearly being left to stew, while he did nothing in particular. He signalled that I should enter. "Now young man, not so long ago I seem to remember telling you I'd be watching your every move. Do you remember that?"

"Yes."

"So what's this?"

He's holding up the big manila envelope containing my suggestion and the relevant data to prove that the suggestion merited the maximum amount of prize money. He's holding it as though it contained dog dirt.

"It's the suggestion I submitted two days ago."

"So you call this a suggestion?"

"Yes."

"Although you've already implemented it without permission?"

"Well that's the only way I could make sure that the idea wouldn't be pinched."

"Who and how would anyone 'pinch' your suggestion?"

"The last time I made a suggestion it was rejected by Rance and Smith. They submitted it a couple of months later and got the prize money. I was making sure that didn't happen again."

"Are you telling me that my foremen stole your suggestion?" He was aggressive and staring at me angrily. I got angry too and boiled over. "Yes, they ripped it off, after telling me it was rejected. They re-wrote it and claimed it as theirs. It's a fiddle, and it's not surprising the only suggestions you get tell you what to do with the suggestion scheme. That's why we never hear of skilled people getting suggestions accepted, just foremen. Cleaners get 'em okay because the foremen cleaners aren't in on the fiddle."

Gallatia, scowling, growled, "Do you want the sack boy?"

I kept my mouth shut because I knew if I said anything I'd insult him and my parents would never forgive me.

"Have you anything to say?"

I gritted my teeth and kept my mouth firmly closed.

"I'm at the end of my tether with you, boy. You've stolen a greasing machine from the scrap company. You've used company time to install it in the sinter plant, without permission, when I'd already made it clear that your employment here was hanging by a thread, and now you expect me to listen to you telling me that my foremen are thieves, and company policies don't work. To top it all you're damn rude to me. I ought to sack you on the spot. You've clearly got talent, but you're rude, insolent, and untrustworthy. Do you think I should sack you?"

I've put up with this terrible place for four and a half long painful years and although I would heave a sigh of relief to leave tomorrow, it does seem stupid to waste all the time spent towards completing an apprenticeship, only to throw it all away with a few ill chosen words, so again I purse my lips and remain silent.

"Go back and get on with your work while I decide what to do with you; and while you're about it, I'll have any paperwork you've put together for this so-called suggestion."

ର୍ଗ୍ର୍ର୍ର

54

Fear & Fiddles; Economics & Ethics

Gallatia knew we had worked miracles in the sinter plant in a very short time. His problem was that we had done it as mavericks, loose cannon, beyond the control of the management, and this he feared and disliked worse than falling profits, a poor safety record or any other of the many ills that might befall a big factory.

The management style was pure Mafia, where the idea of patronage is called respect. Insult the godfather and you're dead. The way the factory was run bore so much resemblance to 1930's Chicago that I felt powerless in the face of gangsters. What was worse was that this was the way it was designed to be. Everyone was frightened, frightened of losing their job, or frightened of being downgraded, or frightened of saying a wrong word. The place was founded on fear and lies and corruption. We had sidestepped rules laid down by the management; rules that existed not for the efficient running of the business, but as an expression of management power. What we'd done showed a lack of fear. Gallatia saw us as drawing pins stuck to his big comfy seat. In their terms we had committed the most heinous crime they could conceive. We were in trouble. Now I understood why I felt uncomfortable about helping Stan to steal the engine and other parts for his car. It wasn't conscience. It was because I had sunk to their level.

164

***

I went to the union meeting that Gilley had told me about and I took the paperwork that Gallatia had told me he wanted. It struck me I knew why he wanted it. The room was full but most of the men there were from other departments, though Banks and Brown were there. The blast furnace worked as an independent unit within the factory and our concerns were different from the men who worked on the line and sometimes our interests were in conflict with the line workers.

The business began with the reading of the agenda. It was a bit like the board meeting of a company. It was all very formal and there was a lot of brother this and brother that which I found weird and stilted, a bit like kids playing black-hand-gang. Then they started to get to the nitty-gritty. The 'brothering' became less prominent as men outside the regular structure began to have their say. Everything became more animated and realistic as the important issues of the day began to be debated and tempers began to flare. I was getting an inkling of what was going on, picking out statements that showed the split between the official union and the shop stewards' committee, of which Banks was one. Brown said nothing. When it was over I hadn't understood a lot of what was going on because I didn't have the background history of events that led to the position as it was. There was the added problem that some issues were not debated at all. The question of Parker, the syndicate, and the under the table goings on that everyone was party to, were not mentioned, but they were important because in some ways they were as much a part of the way the factory worked as clocking in.

Shift payments, agreed procedures, and all the other elements that went to make up the factory were only part of what needed to be considered. When it was over Banks, Brown, Gilley and me went downstairs to the bar. Banks and Brown sat together at one side of the table and Gilley and me sat on the other. Gilley said "What did you make of that, then?" to the table in general. Banks answered "It's the same as usual; the official position is that we all need to toe the line and that means we simply discuss terms within the factory, and politics is out of the window. They know we want to talk politics and they'll even give concessions to stop us. If we can take over the union we can move forward to involving people outside the factory, then we're on our way."

Gilley grunted "Aye well you'll no' get the shop stewards committee running the national union any more than you'll see pigs flying or god on our side. If you want to see real change you'll need to do it outside the union and you'll need a separate organisation. The only way you'll do it is by going to the heart of the matter and taking over the means of production. Lenin's shown the way."

Banks replied, "If you control the union you're on your way to controlling the factory, then you're on the way to controlling the country. Having said that you can't really have socialism in one country."

"Och, you're dreaming. That's ridiculous. The government, the banks and the owners, whether they're shareholders or individuals, are one, and you canna' control one wi'out the other. Stalin may have been a ruthless bastard, but he had no option if he was going to control anti-socialist elements. You canna' do the thing piecemeal. It's got to be all or nothing."

"Hmm, well, we can only agree to disagree. We've been through it often enough. If you're for Stalin, that's up to you I'd rather take my chances with Trotsky."

We talked of generalities and the fact that Gallatia was a thief for withholding our suggestion money. I showed them all the paperwork relating to the suggestion, saying it proved Stan and me had been robbed. Brown studied it in detail but made no comment and would have walked off with it if I hadn't asked for it back.

"Oh sorry," he said as though he'd been absent minded.

We talked of Ted back at work with the two fingers of his left hand there, but virtually useless, banded with pink smooth scar tissue. Butler was mentioned. Brown had been to see him and one side of his

166

face was dented and he said that he'd not been asleep since he came out of the coma. The doctors told him it was because his nerve endings were so disrupted that they no longer joined up properly. Then Banks and Brown left. No one said anything about Fred. He was dead and gone.

I asked Gilley "If you're all Communists, how is it you don't agree?"

"Aye, well, you see it's a wee bit like the Bible. We're Marxists but we interpret Marx in different ways a bit like Catholics and the Church of England. Ah think we need to take over the means of production and develop a planned economy from the bottom up, like Lenin in Russia, though I think it has to be more or less worldwide. Trotskyites, as far as I can make out, believe it can be done through the unions and they argue we need a continuing revolution, whatever that means. Part of why I can't see eye to eye with them is because they can't make it clear to me what they do think, and that's worse than useless. When it comes down to it, decisions need to be made and you can't make good decisions by committee. You canna' design a good car by committee. It's just the same. That's why Ford cars are so poor. No one person designs them so they're neither one thing nor another."

"But what about Parker?" I said.

"He's operating outside of the Company but he needs Gallatia. They're from the same mould. Parker runs what in the war they called the black market. It's just capitalism without us paying taxes. It amounts to the same thing as smuggling. Ordinary people like us get things cheaper. That's why Parker's heavies battered me after the darts match. They're the same sort of people as Hitler or Al Capone. In lots of ways the American government's no better than them. At the end of the war they even used the Mafia to murder communists in Italy then they put their Mafia henchmen back into power. They're still there today, with the blessing of the American government. In the end it comes down to your definition of crime. When the government takes taxes, they're taxes. If the police do a bit independently on the side, it's extortion. Where do you draw the line? When does a grabbing wife become a whore? Parker's is an arrangement that suits everybody but the taxman, and me'be the police, though, chances are some of them are in the know. When is a politician corrupt? Gallatia's part politician and he gets something for turning a blind eye - is that right? Company employees get something over and above their wages - is that right? And Parker's existence doesn't affect the overall running of the factory - is that true? It's what ah call the double standard. Do you know anything about Adam Smith?"

"I've heard the name."

"Aye, well, we all talk about Karl Marx but there was this chap called Adam Smith in about eighteen hundred, old Adam wrote a book called *The Wealth of Nations* and in its way it was every bit as important as Marx's *Capital*. In it he argued everybody won where trade was free. He argued that taxes, subsidies and import duties were bad for all. Before old Adam, people thought they lost out, trading with other countries, because they had to spend cash abroad and it was gone for good but Adam said "If we in England can grow wheat cheaper than they can in France and the French can grow tomatoes cheaper than us, then by swopping tomatoes for wheat both sides gain. Cash makes the transaction possible in just the same way as trading at home." English merchants said, "Yeh, that's right". That argument was what caused the English Civil War. The king said he was boss on a direct mandate from god, and he owned all the land. The merchants argued that wealth came from trade and not necessarily the land. The king wanted to tax the merchants more than the landowners. The merchants won the civil war that wasn't really settled till the repeal of the Corn Laws that were a subsidy for farmers, who, when you came down to it, were the old aristocracy. But when it came to the British Empire the merchants became 'Bleed 'em white tax collectors'. The only difference was instead of ripping people off just in England, like the old aristocracy, they were doing it all over the empire. Here's the same old double standard. That's the part of the industrial revolution that no one talks about. They call it imperialism, and leave it at that.

Raw greed and raw power are different sides of the same coin, but they conflict one with the other.'

On the one hand the Company stands for capitalism and free trade, but on the other it stands for old-fashioned power-wielding corruption, just the same as common or garden gangsters. That's where 'kiss my arse' Gallatia comes in. That's a large part of why big companies have trouble keeping up with the times. They're there so that the bosses can be bosses, and profit is only part of the reason.

"So you think Gallatia's plain crooked then, and playing both ends against the middle?"

"If you think Gallatia's straight, lad, he's cleverer than I thought. He's as crooked as the thread on a bent bolt. He's followed such a crooked road, he does ney know where he's been. It's the same with the Labour Party and unions. Those with power at the top think they're something special and expect to be admired thinking their positions should be aspired to by the lower orders. They're infected with the same double standard that applies to the bosses. What you're looking for is democracy lad, and finding it is no' easy because in the end we're all crooks and the real basis of the system we've got now is the control of criminality with laws that stop it going too far and making life hell for everybody. It's mah opinion that Russia is going the right way though."

"How do you work that out?"

"The Labour Party and the unions are a waste of time if you want socialism lad. The truth is, they're a sham. You canna' half accept socialism. You either buy the whole deal or reject the lot. You have to make a choice; truth, justice and freedom, or repression, lies and chains. Where do concessions end and corruption begin? Wars across the world are out of date. Wars are fought over property or territory. Where you've got multi-nationals, territory's of no matter. Only wealth and power are important because territory is valueless without people. It's the kind of people you're dealing with that's the significant thing. When people place more value on truth, justice and freedom than on greed and power, the greedy and powerful find them

169

ungovernable. That's what happened in Russia under the Tzar. Men began to wonder why they were first nearly starved to death and then sent to the front with one gun between three. They realised the Tzars had created a fabulous myth about what mattered. They were offered three options: stay at home and be shot as a draft dodger; hide and starve to death; or go to the front to get killed - death, death or death. The chances are, if it happened to you, you'd start looking for alternatives. That's the real reason Russia became communist. That's the real reason we got the National Health Service and growth economics. We get two percent a year to feed avarice and greed. D'you understand that?"

"Yeah I've read about Keynes and Myrdle and cutting tariff barriers to stop recessions. It sounds like your bloke Adam Smith."

"Aye, that's right and they put Keynes over as socialist with Attlee and the Labour Party but they're pulling the wool. Adam Smith is really and truly the father of capitalism. Before Smith, money lending for interest, cornering the market to raise prices, and watering beer and the like were all illegal and immoral. Muslims still stick to those ideas, more or less, but according to Adam they're all fair game. Putting the law the old way made greed immoral, but after Adam greed became good trade, and the whole system was turned on its head and greed became good business and beneficial for all. The odd thing is that to a degree it's true. That's the real reason the German and Japanese economies are doing so well. That's what the Marshall Plan is all about. Either living standards improve, or there's every chance people'll go communist. The rich and powerful bit the bullet with the war and gave us massive concessions, with free education and the NHS. They made all of us in the so-called 'civilised' West complicit in milking not only the people of the rest of the world, but the resources of the world itself. We're all capitalists now. They've been trying to take those concessions back ever since. The irony is that Adam Smith is right, and if you take capitalism to its logical conclusion you finish up with socialism, because the foundation of his argument has to be: everyone should start out on a level playing field.

170

What screws things up is inheritance and silver spoons. Do away with that and you do away with big factories that are far and away the most efficient way of doing things, though there can be little doubt that land should be rented out by the state and not passed on by inheritance. We're no longer living in a tribal society, where peasants subsist on their own piece of land. When all's said and done, there are no complete answers, lad. We just have to do our best and honesty's the thing. End corruption and you'll solve most of the world's problems."

"Hm, well, I'll have to think about it but it sounds mostly convincing." I finished my drink and stood up to leave. I was thinking it might sound better than it really was, posing more questions than it answered.

ↀↀↀↀ

55

Deference and Deviousness

The more I thought about it, most of what Gilley said made sense. What Gallatia really wanted was deference. He really believed that I should have approached the management 'cap in hand,' suggesting that we fit a greasing machine in the sinter plant to save the company money. I think they would have rejected the idea out of hand.

"Huh, that won't work," would almost certainly have been the response. Had this not been the case, then Gallatia would have regarded the acceptance of my idea as the spreading of a kind of largesse for which I should be eternally grateful. The approbation of the management in Gallatia's opinion should be enough to satisfy my pride, ego, self esteem, power seeking or greed, whatever you want to call it. As Tom Wyatt would graphically put it, he wanted me to 'suck arse.'

171

The true objective of the suggestion scheme was to give the impression that their only aim was improved efficiency. The real motives were far more complicated.

I decided that it wasn't me who was rude, insolent, arrogant, sly and untrustworthy, but Gallatia himself. He was using raw power to deny me what was rightfully mine. The very existence of a suggestion scheme gave me the right to expect that my suggestion be considered properly, on its merits. Previous events had shown this would not be the case and I could prove it. To organize things the way I had, in the light of the circumstances, was perfectly reasonable. Gallatia, by rejecting my submission, had reneged on the very idea of a suggestion scheme. He might just as well have said, 'Heads I win; tails you lose'.

This conclusion left me in a quandary. The business of deference and patronage clearly made the organization less effective at achieving its stated aims. Did this make the stated aims different from the real aims? Where did I go from there?

The answer seemed to be beyond the bounds of reason, because the actions of management didn't appear rational. Their twin objectives of power and profit were in conflict. Which would they put first? The answer in this instance was power, but it could well have been profit, especially if the decision had been taken nearer the top of the hierarchy.

***

By three o' clock that afternoon Stan had been called to the main office and informed that from the following Monday, he'd be working back at the main workshop.

172

56

An ex-Muslim Christian Replaces Stan and back to a 'Pool' System

Monday May 9th 8.10 a.m. 1966:

Stan's gone and Rance has just arrived. Trailing behind him is a skinny Asian. Looking embarrassed and flustered Rance says,

"This is Mohammed Khan. You'll be his mate from now on." He didn't say Khan would be in charge. Turning to Mohammed and motioning him to come forward, he introduced us.

"Mohammed, this is Dave. He'll show you what to do." I'm still burning at the thought that Stan has been simply removed without any discussion. We're being treated like cards in a game of patience.

"I can't do that; he must be the fitter if I'm still an apprentice." Rance replied. "He is a fitter but he'll need showing around the plant. When he knows what machines he's supposed to be dealing with, he'll be okay." With that he sheepishly walked off. I was steaming mad, shouting after him, "You're a gutless thieving twat," still with the pinched suggestion niggling away in my mind. He continued walking, his back hunched in embarrassment, tacit proof of the truth of my words. Turning my anger on Mohammed, I asked, "And you. What the fuck do you know about fitting?"

"Oh yes I am understanding the fitting. I am learning in the engine sheds in Darjeeling. I am getting very qualified fitter in India. I am doing the much precision work on the steam engines." He was smiling in a simpering way bowing and scraping as if I was in charge and he some kind of servant. I was sick of him already. I suppose I like a bit of insolence. There's something upright and honest about it, not like this character, oozing backstabbing deviousness.

I had to go to the stores and talked with him, explaining the functions of the different buildings on the way. By the time we'd got there I'd established that he'd converted from being a Muslim to

Christianity and he'd got this job through contacts at his church. It seemed to me he might be using religion as a tool for social advancement. I can't help feeling prejudiced against him. There was a gut feeling I had that he was as trustworthy as a mastiff in a butchers. I'd yet to prove it on the job, but I had a nasty feeling he would be as useful as a primed grenade stitched in my 'Y' fronts.

***

Mohammed had only been with me a couple of days when Bernie in the by-products was off sick (probably to keep his pension intact) and a gland was leaking excessively on a big gas pump. When I say big, I mean big. It was about twelve feet tall and probably weighed in at twenty tons. It was the thing that pushed the gas from Fords into the national grid.

Rance moved Mohammed and me to fix it. The job wasn't difficult, just heavy. The pressure plate was in two halves, each weighing ten or fifteen pounds, and they were awkward to get at. The top one came out quite easily but the bottom was proving to be a pig. Mohammed was on the other side of the machine and we were pulling together. He wasn't a lot of help. I don't think he was trying very hard, but suddenly out it came, all of a rush, and pinned my arm inside the machine. I shouted to him to come round to my side and help me get it off, but nothing happened. My intuition was right.

I could feel blood trickling around my wrist, although my arm was going numb. I don't know how long he took, but he'd gone to the main workshop to get help and left me standing with this great weight cutting into my arm. He was gone for a quarter of an hour at least. He came back with one of the labourers from the main workshop. I was released quite easily with the labourer helping me to lift the plate. Mohammed didn't help. He stood by, dumb, hopeless and useless. The damage to my arm wasn't great, but it could have been. I might have been mildly in shock. I felt a bit sick. I was less than delighted with Mohammed's performance.

Two days later I sent him to the stores. After three hours he still hadn't returned and I set off in search. I'd not gone a hundred yards before I came upon him. He was squatting on his haunches, chatting to one of his countrymen. I saw red and ran up behind him and kicked him as if he were a football. Screaming "Get on with it, you lazy bastard." He went sprawling. I shouldn't have done it, but - oh, it was satisfying. I carried on walking because I knew if he said anything I might let fly at him again. At the stores I learned that he'd not even got that far. I collected the parts I needed, and returned to the sinter plant, to be summoned to Gallatia's office.

"Mr Kahn has made a complaint, saying you kicked him. Is that true?"said Gallatia while Rance stood behind him blank faced.

"Yes, but I was provoked."

"And what form did this provocation take?"

"Two days ago he contributed to this." I displayed my bandaged arm.

"And today I sent him to the stores. I went looking for him after three hours, to find him chattering, still not having gone to the stores. He was squatting on the ground and I kicked him to get him moving."

"Is this true, Mr Kahn?"

"Oh I was not three hours. Oh no. I had not been gone long time. I did speak to my friend but it was not a lot of time I was spending, and then he come along and he kick me. I am thinking he is not liking my colour. He does not like me," he said, simpering and half sneering. If I got too near I might vomit and I knew where I'd aim. It could be almost as satisfying as kicking him.

"Is this true, Mr Ray? Do you feel animosity towards Mr Kahn because of his colour?"

"I couldn't care less if he's all the colours of the rainbow, so long as he does his work."

"Are you prepared to apologise to Mr Kahn?"

"I don't mind apologising but I won't work with him again. He's a bloody liability. You'll have to dump him on some other poor

175

sod."

"That's enough of that."

"Mr Kahn, are you prepared to accept an apology?"

"I am accepting an apology but I cannot work with this man. He does not like me."

"All right. Ray, apologise, and the pair of you shake hands."

"I apologise," I said with contempt. And as we shook hands I gritted my teeth, gripping his hand across the knuckles with all my strength, until he winced.

That's it, I'm on my own, I thought. Kahn went in front of me. He'd not learnt his lesson. If we'd been alone I'd have kicked his skinny arse again. As he left, Gallatia called,

"Ray." There was a pause as I turned. "What is it with you? You're not stupid, but wherever you are, there's trouble. I'm going to move you into the drawing office, where I can see you. You'll be placed in charge of a contract. This is your last chance, boy. Put one foot wrong and you're out. Do - you - understand - me?" with long pauses for emphasis. I didn't understand why he didn't sack me there and then. I wanted to say "Go - fuck - your - self", with pauses to match his, but merely answered, "Yes."

There was an uncharacteristic hint of hesitancy in his manner. "Right, you'll answer to Mr Wilkinson. Go and get your things then see Mr Jones about a locker and remember, the slightest trouble from you, and you're out. Consider yourself on probation for the next six months."

I can remeber thinking. Goodbye sinter plant. Goodbye Stan's pleasant company. Goodbye suggestion money. Goodbye 'la dolce vita.' Hello 'Pride comes before a fall.' If I had a tail it would have been paralysed, rigid between my legs. Probation again - but why didn't he sack me?

57

Wilko's World

Monday May 23rd 1966 8.00 a.m.

My mother is pleased. I've got a different clocking in card. I'm still T1052, but the new card is white instead of the standard factory brown manilla. Wow, I'm really going places.

I'm back in the drawing office and expected to wear a collar and tie. I feel constricted, almost worse than if it was jail. I sit on a high drawing office type chair in full view of Gallatia. I wonder if he's been reading Dickens. I don't have to put my hand up when I want to go to the toilet, the way they do on the production line, but I've just got to scratch my nose to feel his malevolent eye following every move I make. Thank heaven I'll be able to escape sometimes. I have to see contractors and go out into the plant to take measurements so, if I get really desperate, I'll be able to fabricate some excuse.

There's a view if I crane my neck around the drawing board. Through the window I can see the back of the power station and the sinter plant fan casing. Everything is black and grey or rust streaked brown. Every so often a cloud of grey smoking coke dust showers onto the railway line outside, as another thirty tons of red-hot coke is ejected from the retorts across the road. Thank god there is the light of early summer; in winter the sight would be totally demoralising.

I have been given a job ensuring the contractors fabricating a stand for a huge iron ladle are meeting specifications laid down by the company. These ladles weigh two hundred tons loaded, so the thing will be big and solid. I haven't worked it out but I guess it'll weigh about ten tons. The drawings have already been made. I have to check them, then liaise with a firm down the road that will make it. I have other things to do but they're just odds and ends of hack drawing office work. I'm edgy about what's going on. I am still an apprentice but I'm being asked to do the sort of work only someone qualified should be doing. Gallatia's the boss, so I've no option but to get on with it.

It's a great pleasure to be clean, but my mother has talked me into getting a new nylon shirt. It makes me stink. It's horrible and will go straight in the bin as soon as I can get it off. I think it must have been designed to make the wearer sticky and sweaty as part of devious plan to sell deodorant. The office is hot and stuffy too. Maybe some-one here also has shares in a deodorant company.

These shirts are being sold hard; there's lots of advertising. They're easy to wash, and quick to dry. They need to be, they need washing about once an hour. Around here they're not popular because if it rains and your house is downwind of Fords foundry, the rain is so full of sulphur dioxide that it makes sulphuric acid strong enough to burn holes in nylon. The women daren't put their stockings on the washing line because they don't get runs, they simply disintegrate. The paint and chrome on cars is affected too. Eventually something will have to be done but at the moment the company is simply denying responsibility. No doubt when the rain starts damaging the cars in the stock car parks, then they'll set about de-toxifying our rain.

***

The job is going well. The cradle is all but finished. The biggest problem is making sure the bolts that attach it to the floor match the holes in its base. I've overcome this by getting the fabricators to make a plywood jig using the actual base as a pattern. A local civil engineering firm will carry out the installation and they will have the pattern to work to when they pour concrete. If the bolts in the floor don't match the holes in the cradle, it will be their problem. The fabricators complained because I had changed the spec', asking for the jig to be made, but the original contract included the price of painting. We agreed to forego the paint and use the cash saved to pay for the jig.

Paint was pointless. The thinnest plate on the thing is half an inch. It will be under cover, so corrosion isn't a consideration. At present the job is ahead of schedule and everybody is happy. I'm staying out of the office as much as possible. Gallatia's eyes spit threat and malevolence whenever our glances clash.

I have to see the hot metal shed foreman today, about the exact positioning of the cradle. I'll be back in overalls for that. The place is full of treacherous soft graphite. The floor is like a skating rink. When I first went there, it was quite a novelty, just like being in the playground at school on a frosty morning, when we used to make great long slides and raced to see who could slide furthest (Mum used to go mad when I arrived home with my shoes in tatters). After a while my legs ache with the constant tension needed to retain my balance. The furnace-men wear heavy wooden clogs with bars of metal nailed across the soles, that give a better grip than my rubber soles. Anything and everything the graphite touches is irreversibly contaminated. Looking in a mirror I might have been rolling in soft pencil lead. At the slightest touch it embeds itself in skin. At first it looks as though I've got pencil lead patches but then it goes black and ingrained in the pores. Soap makes hardly any impression at all.

I should have waited till now to throw away the nylon shirt; I'd have saved myself some earache from Mum that way. The building is hot and cold by turns. The wind whistles through the open ends of the huge shed. When they're not pouring metal, it's almost dark. There are only a few fluorescent tubes high up, and you freeze. When they 'pour,' the furnace hearth bursts into life like the stage at the theatre when the curtain goes up. All of a rush, it's tremendously hot; everything glows orange or red and the silhouettes of men move purposefully against the glow. Sparks float around, cooling to settle as tiny glittering flakes of graphite. It's spectacular to watch.

To tap the furnace a sacrificial tube called a thermic lance is lit at the end burning acetylene and oxygen. They say safebreakers have used these lances. I can't believe it. The stink would be phenomenal and both safe and contents would be destroyed in no time. It generates astounding heat, melting both the clay in the tap hole and the tube itself. Two or three men swathed in great leather aprons, wearing heavy gauntlets, and clogs with thick leather uppers, their faces covered by shiny masks that vividly reflect flaming orange as they push for all they are worth, passing the tube hand over hand as it melts. The heat is breathtaking. Suddenly they break through and molten iron bursts out in a great fountain of sparks, to flow fast like fresh liquid lava into the huge ladles on special railway trucks below.

Dazzling showers of sparks surround the whole operation. When the 'pour' is finished the slag that follows the iron is redirected by a sluice into another ladle, to be dumped into a pond, like the one I ran across when I was still in the Trade School, to solidify and be broken up like block toffee for road-stone. To staunch the flow, a massive piece of machinery swings into action on a great hinge, to squeeze fireclay into the tap-hole like a giant toothpaste tube. A motor that on its own must weigh tons, applies pressure through a screw over a foot in diameter. Everything in and about the place is enormous. I was there last week when somebody from Scotland Yard, all dressed in lovely white overalls, was watching as a consignment of guns was thrown into a ladle of molten iron to simply melt and be incorporated into next week's cars.

***

We're committed… the hole is dug and the day after tomorrow, if all goes to plan, the civil engineering crew will be pouring concrete. Their men complained about the working conditions, mainly, I think, with reference to the graphite. I believe their company agreed to pay some dirt money or something, but there have been no major problems digging the pit for the base.

Monday evening. Job done. The cradle is installed and tested The concrete isn't as hard as it will be. The crane driver was very careful and lowered the two hundred ton ladle as slowly and gently as if he were lowering it onto an egg and wanted to stop at the exact moment the shell cracked. The floor withstood the load okay so now I'm looking for the next job. I've had no communication from Gallatia yet, though he knows the job's complete. I think he's leaving me in suspense again. I guess he's enjoying exercising his power this way.

***

No camaraderie around the punch-clock now, only the prospect of an interview with Wilko and perhaps Mr Gallatia. There are a couple of other people in the office but we don't talk much. I have the feeling they don't want anything to do with me. I think they're worried about catching a nasty dose of dissent or discontent, or failing that, a knife in the back. There's an atmosphere of political tension here you could cut with that very same knife. There are undercurrents I feel but don't understand. The other two don't exactly send me to Coventry but they communicate with nothing beyond odd pleasantries. The order of the day here is – 'If in doubt, say nowt.' This isn't a great problem for me. One is a fifty-year-old nonentity called Small, doing hackwork and serving out the time until he retires with the resignation of a whipped dog. The other is odd. He must have a past. He comes on a train every day from Richmond, on the other side of London, to work in this hellhole. The trip takes him two hours each way and must cost a fortune. His name's Gerrard; he's far too well spoken to work here. He progresses jobs and contracts and deals with ordering materials. He sits in his little corner hardly talking to anyone, beavering away. It looks like a boring job to me but he's a mystery man and there's something about him that makes me think he's not boring at all. Intuition tells me he's brim full of pent up frustration. He never looks well, he's thin, almost cadaverous, and his gaunt cheeks are marked with red spots, like a coughing TB patient. Its not makeup. He's not odd that way but always twitching and edgy, hardly surprising, since he can have virtually no time for a life of his own, other than weekends. He's an enigma if ever there was one. No one really

181

knows him at all.

Mrs Short, Gallatia's secretary, raises her eyebrows and pulls a prissy face that goes with the sort of woman who'd wave a Union Jack at a coronation. She's trying to indicate I'm honoured, as she tells me to go to Wilkinson's office for instructions regarding the next job. There's not a lot going on behind her eyes; they flicker like a failing bulb when she blinks which she does too long and too often. She's proud of herself, imagining she's important in the place. Gallatia treats her like a dog and talks to her as if she's a Dictaphone machine. I wonder how long it'll be before the light goes out completely.

I knock. Wilko absent-mindedly calls. "Come in". As I step through the door he's facing me behind his chair, studying the layout of his lunchbox, tobacco tin, cigarette lighter and pen and pencil. These items are spread in a neat row across his otherwise bare desk, more or less equally spaced apart. He stands back to survey his desk, like an artist getting a different perspective on his work, then, leaning forward over his chair, ignoring me, he moves the pen an eighth of an inch to the left. He turns away from me, then suddenly, as if to catch his possessions in the act of moving like naughty schoolboys, quickly turns to face me again, and for the second time in twenty seconds he carefully leans over the back of his chair to move the pencil, this time just a tiny fraction to the left. This ritual is a normal beginning to Wilko's day. His name ought to be Wacko Wilko; he's half crazy and close to cracking up completely.

The more the men hate him the more irascibly unreasonable he gets. The measure by which they hate him is displayed by events last week when someone put shit in his lunchbox. Even in this place a thing like that wasn't done lightly. Someone would happily see him dead. I think he's on a downward spiral to his own private hell.
Turning his desiccated face to me without any acknowledgment his behaviour is odd, he says, "Ah yes, Ray, got another little contract for you to deal with. It's the ore yard crane. It's been due for painting for a while now. Simple job, just chip rust spots, wire brush, single coat of red oxide on the rust spots then two coats of undercoat all over and

one top coat. Paint's specified as well, we just want you to oversee the job. Here's the spec,' handing me a folder. 'Slater's the contractor. Any questions, come and see me. You'd better get over there now, they're due to start this morning."

"Right, okay then, I'd better go."

The interview is over, he returns to his private world where he spends a growing amount of time living with who knows what thoughts of his own. This is normal Wilko, he's either more or less angry or in this other world.

I'm happy to get away from the crazy bastard, but what the hell are they playing at. I've had no time to check the spec' or anything; it's bloody ludicrous. I rush to get my overalls on and see what's going on.

***

"Stop. Stop. What do you think you're doing." There are two men here wearing throwaway paper overalls with hoods attached. They are wielding two soft brooms dipping them into a ten gallon tin of paint and pushing the paint along as though sweeping up a flood. Thank god they've not been here long; they're already covered in paint and it's going everywhere. There's almost as much on the ground as on the crane. The person in charge is facing me with an expression, part sneer, part aggression, and part aggrieved.

"We bin' told ter get paint on this fing quick as possible an' we're doin' it. What the fuckin' 'ell's the problem?"

"The problem is this." I've brought the specification folder with me, and hold out it towards him.

"What's that then?" Looking at me with what appears to be genuine almost comic puzzlement.

"It's a job spec". "You don't know about job specs' ?"

"I'm a fuckin' painter mate. Tosher if yer like. Me an' 'im, we get paint on fings an' we specialise in doin' it fuckin' quick. We do stations, pylons an' fings like this crane, nuffin' fancy, jist quick an'

183

we ain't gonna ge' it done fuckin' readin".

"Well you'd better stop doing this quick, cos' you're not meeting the spec' and look at the mess you're making; it's even going on cars down there".

"Well the fuckin' cars shouldn't be there, should they? Even we've not bin allahed t' park there an' we've 'ad ter lug the fuckin' paint 'alf a bleedin' mile 'fore startin' ter climb this bleedin' fing wiv it, an' we was told we could 'ave a cradle, an' we can't 'cos the fuckin' fing keeps movin', an' we shouldn't be workin' on it while it's runnin' 'cos' it's too fuckin' dangerous."

"Right, well you'd better stop, and I'll go and see my boss and see what's to be done".

"Well, yer better fuckin' 'urry up cos we're on bonus an' we aint fuckin' 'angin' abaht 'ere all bleedin' day."

There's no way you'd call me middle class, but this character comes from another planet. All he needs is a tail and he could dispense with a cradle.

After jogging back to the office I arrive to find Wilko' out. Mrs Short has no idea where he is so what am I to do? Dump the problem on Rance? I don't have the authority to deal with it so let some other poor sod carry the can. My luck's in - Rance is in the main workshop office. I simply recount to him what's going on with the crane and leave it at that, having let him know that the contractors are simply not paying any attention to the spec' sheet whatsoever. I leave a note for Wilco to cover myself.

184

58

Limbo Again, Gerrard Gets Chatty
and Real Resposibility

Monday August 1st 1966 8.10 a.m

I'm back in limbo again - god knows what'll happen next. I've odd jobs to do but nothing like real work, so it's sit in the office doing 'make work' drawing office jobs. At the end of a day I feel shattered, having done virtually nothing and always there's the knowledge that Gallatia is just yards away watching, watching. I've not been in long and I'm still considering how to shape my day when Gerrard comes across to my drawing board from his private admin' corner. He's never spoken more than twenty words to me before today, but this morning he's quite chatty. He starts talking about the sinter plant greasing machine and what a success it is and how he knows because the orders for the bearings have dropped right off and it's saving a fortune. Then he tells me he's interested to see the records I kept. I tell him that I've left them in a locked cupboard in the sinter plant workshop. A lot of people are showing a hell of a lot of interest in those records: I wonder why.

***

In some ways being stuck in this office is worse than crownwheels. It's too hot and I'm bored sick. Silly though it may sound, I'm itching and dying for proper useful work. But I'll not give up now, the apprentice-ship's cost me too much already, and there is just a year to go before I get the piece of paper that says I'm a skilled man. I'm counting the days, hours and minutes. The second I get that paper in my hand, I'll be gone from this dreadful place.

At last - another proper job and what a job; the brief is brought to me by Mrs Short. That's odd. She comes from Gallatias office and hands me the spec' sheets saying, "These are the specification sheets for the next project you're to oversee. Mr Gallatia has asked me to give them to you and at the same time he has asked me to remind you that he wants the data you collected to support what you did in fitting the greasing machine in the sinter plant." When she's finished she draws a big breath. She's good at repeating instructions verbatim but it requires that she raises her head to the ceiling closes her eyes and clasps her hands as though she's praying. I place my hands together as though joining her in prayer and give a small bow, but it's lost on her. She just looks a little bemused and her eyes find the floor as they flicker with a series of worried blinks.

The brief is basically the same as the ladle-cradle and paint contracts. My role will be to control contractors, making sure that agreed specifications are met in a timely and efficient manner. They're the words used in the contract somewhere, pleasingly concise, unlike so much of the other legalistic gobbledegook. This time I've had proper warning and been given the spec' sheets in plenty of time to allow me to become familiar with what is required. This work takes me from the sublime to the ridiculous; the responsibility is frightening. It's madness putting an apprentice in charge of something as big as this. I'm getting close to a good wage now, over eleven hundred pounds a year. That's the one good thing about working here; the money is better than anywhere else in the area.

This is a thirty thousand pound contract and I'm to be the person controlling how it's brought to a conclusion. The task is to convert the Sultzer Plant building where red hot coke ejected from the retorts was used to preheat the water supply to the power station. The building has been abandoned for years, but is immensely strong. It's built like an air raid shelter, with lots of reinforced concrete. Converting it into a washroom and locker room with showers and toilets is quite a challenge. One thing's certain - we won't have to worry about overloading the floors. This is a significant contract, much bigger than painting the crane.

That work incidentally has not been finished. The job simply stopped. Quite what went on I've never discovered. All that's left is one section of the crane covered in a gobby mess a lighter colour than the rest. It's never been finished. I'm just glad I escaped without repercussions. I still think something fishy was going on, but I guess I'll never know. That Gallatia wants the figures I put together for the greaser suggestion is interesting. That's the second or is it the third time he's asked, and Brown and Gerrard seemed dead interested too.

This new business is entirely different. It involves a lot, much of which is completely outside the area of mechanical engineering and outside my experience, making it all the more frightening. For a start there is what they call groundwork to do; drains and a water supply have to be connected. All I know about drains is they stink. There are other implications, as well. Our site is almost on a level with the river so somewhere pumps must be involved. I'll need to pick the brains of the contractors and hope I ask the right questions. An electricity supply also needs connecting, but that doesn't represent such a problem because the electricity board will be overseeing that part of the job. I've actually got access to a quantity surveyor's report, which prices the job at around twenty seven thousand pounds. The company uses a three-quote system, taking the middle quote as the one that is most realistic. This seems sensible, but given the management's attitude to cash I find it surprising. I really can't believe they don't simply take the cheapest price.

The lowest quote is just over twenty seven thousand, the one that got the business is three thousand pounds more at just over thirty. The highest is just under thirty-one. All these prices seem exorbitant, but the cost of the groundwork is a mystery to me, so I assume they're reasonable. We're due to start in a week's time and the whole contract is scheduled to take three months. I've chatted to Bernie about the way the contracts are won. He says as often as not in *Fords,* they're fiddled. Palms are greased and the 'right' contractor gets the job because he knows what to quote. Bernie's dad owns a garage in Dagenham. He's the only person I know who has any dealings at the top end of the business scale and I guess there's probably some truth in what he says. I can't wait to start. Fiddles or not and scary or not,

I'm getting blisters on my backside sitting here with no proper work to do, and Gallatia looking at me as though he wished he could pull the chain and flush me away.

I've been given the drawings showing exactly how the job is to be done, and have set about marking out in chalk the spots where concrete has to be cut away. It sounds easy, but it's even easier to make a mistake. I'm taking great care to make sure everything is okay regarding the drawings. I've heard some fantastic horror stories of monumental cock-ups, like drawings read the wrong way round so one floor is right handed and the floor above left handed, so that the stair wells are diametrically opposite, making it necessary to do the whole job again. I can't afford anything like that happening and I'm aware of my inexperience doing this sort of work. I'm slow to begin with, and having to check, check and check makes me even slower and saps my confidence. 'Measure twice cut once' in mind I measure half a dozen times and still worry. At least no one is bothering me so far, and I'm away from Gallatia.

On the way here I met Stan who was with me in the sinter plant. We were chatting just as if we were still working together. He holds no grudges and regards the whole episode as a chapter that's finished. He was saying he thinks the system where fitters are autonomous is slyly being changed again back to a pool. The new system works better but the management can't maintain control so easily and it irks them terribly. He's fed up with the whole place and thinking of moving on, although he's been here sixteen years and knows all the wrinkles, and won't be able to get anything like the money he gets here. He said he thinks the only person who is in any sort of position to cope is Bernie. Because of his war pension, it's difficult for them to push him around because they can't sack him easily the way they can the rest of us. For us it's do their bidding or you're out and all the time they're getting better at watching. They've even approached the union wanting to fit cameras at the doors of the toilets, so visits can be timed. Talk about sick. Join the Ford racing crap challenge. There'll be a strike if they do, the bastards. I'm due to meet the main contractor's site foreman this afternoon. I hope I get on okay with him.

59

Who Am I? Where Am I? A Girl & Me.

Friday September 9th 1966

I've been a few times to the Flamingo Club at Wardour Street in London with Allie' from school. We're off again tonight. I'm feeling a bit edgy. It's 'the place to be', but a bit wild. Allie's family come from Shoreditch and they maintain their links with the East End, so there's something different about their house compared with ours. At Allie's there's an awareness of social activity that has no place at home. I'm told to keep my nose clean and mouth shut; 'If anyone asks, you're C. of E.', is what I've been told since I was a kid. The world isn't supposed to impinge on our family. Religion, politics and social interaction are there, but not acknowledged. I can't disregard these things. Life without discussion of books, the news, music, or anything you care to think of, is arid. I live in the world and need to express myself freely, be it through painting, writing or simply talking. I might talk rubbish but that's my right and a right to be enjoyed. I'm not a piece of tracing paper that people can see through, almost as though I'm not there. Crosswords and playing cards aren't enough. I think my mother feels the same but suppresses the feeling, and it costs her dear.

We were all sitting around the fire one night and mum suddenly flung out her arm crying out "Ooh, ooh, ooh." Her outstretched arm shook her whole body for seconds. It was so sudden and shocking, we took time to realise that something was seriously wrong. We were at a loss what to do. "What's the matter? What's the matter?" we were asking. She settled and relaxed. "I've gone all numb down one side, ooh, ooh. I've gone all numb.' She was flushed with fear and worry. We made her tea and asked if we should call the doctor but she said "No. It's going off. I'll be all right." She didn't even go to the doctor's and it was no good trying to force her, but I'm sure she'd had a small stroke and I don't think it's the first either. I think it might have something to do with bottling her feelings and frustrations in order to keep the peace, whilst dangerously raising her blood pressure.

***

Georgie Fame is the resident artist at the Flamingo and Alistair, who lives near Allie's, plays the drums there, so we have connections. Allie' is a 'Mod' ahead of the Mods. His cousin's a shoe designer and he's commissioned a pair of shoes made from real crocodile skin that cost a fortune, and he's had a suit made from lovat green Harris Tweed with an old style flap front instead of a fly, as well as a four inch waist band. It's a bit excessive and exhibitionist but beauty is in the eye of the beholder. It's a funny thing, but Allie's a quiet sort of lad, quieter than me; I only get confident when I get mad. The truth is we're from Dagenham and trained to think we're not very bright. Allie's family have a tradition of sharp dressing. Allie and I were walking up the street once behind a little fellow walking with a bounce and a swagger. He was wearing a pork pie hat at a jaunty angle, tight trousers and a nifty three-quarter-length coat. I judged him to be a 'Jack the lad' thirty year old. We walked past him and Allie said "Hello, Grandad, how are you?" I thought he was messing around but then I saw the face. It **was** Allie's Grandad. He was over seventy and still after the girls. He's a character. He could carry off being a pearly king.

I try to keep up with fashion. It's not so easy for me because at our house clothes are durable, reasonably priced and 'sensible', fashion doesn't come into it. As a kid I wore what I was given. There were no ifs or buts so fashion's all new to me. I ordered a suit from the Jewish tailor in Barking where my Dad had his made. The result is something with padded shoulders a little less pronounced than an American footballer's, with a jacket that's tapered all the way to where it stops three inches below the waist. The trousers are tapered in a way that makes me look wedge shaped from the shoulders down. All I need is a pork pie hat with a tartan band and some pointed shoes and I'd look as though I'm trying for the look of a spivvy version of the Cray Twins. It cost a months' wages and I wore it once to a wedding. I was so embarrassed I can't wear it again. I don't want some nut trying to prove he's a hard man taking me on with a razor to prove it, so I 'make do' wearing Ben Sherman and Madras cotton shirts and a thin, decidedly eye-catching darkish multi coloured Paisley patterned jacket that I roll up small and keep hidden so that my parents won't know. I think if they saw it they might worry I'm one of 'them'. On nights out I wear this with either plum coloured or black cords and a pair of really soft black leather boots with elastic sides and broad chisel toes. Dad calls them my club feet. I like them a lot. They've got real style and thin real leather soles. They're dead comfortable.

Despite being 'moddish' as regards our clothes, both Allie and me ride motorbikes, because we have engineering jobs and think scooters are rubbish pieces of engineering. Not many people know that the engine of the Vespa scooter began life as the starter motor of a wartime aircraft and has been used to power scooters as a makeshift to keep the factory going since the war. Fashion is important, but neither of us allow it to interfere with our appreciation of the basics of our transport. Scooters are crap.

I'm not a great fan of music of any sort, but there is something about the Flamingo. It's fashionable and carries us along, exciting and dynamic and most of all an escape from mundane work in rotten East End factories. Partly it's about drugs - dope and speed - though the music is special. The dancing goes on until early morning and the last train home is at eleven. It's either that or a taxi home that none of us can afford. Drugs are part of what's going on. Purple Hearts and Paris

191

Blues keep us buzzing till the tube starts again in the morning. The pills don't do a lot for the sex drive. John Thomas down below is as lively as a wet detonator but that doesn't stop things in your head.

There's a girl. She's delicious. She's not a tremendous 'looker' but she's beautiful. Her face has character. She's not got film starry looks, all perfect regular features, hair held together with glue and a bland empty face. She's got a square jaw that could look weird and makes me think she could be obstinate; that could cause the sparks to fly but I have a feeling she'd win. She'd just have to do something with her mouth, It's too wide, dead sexy, and opens her whole face up when she smiles or laughs. She's got brown eyes, dark but fiery. I'm not sure if she knows, but she's only got to do this wrinkle her face up thing that she does now and then as she's talking and it kills me. Most of the time she looks as though there's something going on that surprises her. There's something fresh, naive and virginal about her. She's not all plastered with makeup like a lot of the Dagenham girls. She has lovely velvet skin that's slightly translucent, like bone china, showing a hint of bluish veins beneath. Makeup would ruin it. I can't help forgiving her smoking too much. It almost heightens the feeling she gives of not having enough time to fit everything in.

She's constantly moving her light boned mysterious female body with unbridled enthusiasm for everything about her. Every so often she does something that reminds me of Mum's Dad. She has the same sort of sparkle. I have this thing where I kind of prod people winding them up to get a reaction. I can't help it. It just happens. It's part of the way I am. She's the same and winding her up just makes her more enthusiastic, that's why I do it. I've never thought about it before. People take offence at things I say sometimes. I'm learning to be careful because it's a kind of arrogance. I don't do it to annoy them but it gets them going and they get annoyed like Dad. With Diane it's different. We strike sparks off one another; it's fantastic. She's not dull like so many other girls I've met. I can talk to her, really talk to her. We're on exactly the same wavelength. I've never felt so at home with anyone. We laugh at the same things and we're

192

interested in the same things. I'm not usually relaxed with girls but there are no chat-up lines, it just happens. We're talking about anything and everything for hours. We're friends in minutes.

I'm a rubbish dancer. Dancing should have a formality about it. There should be patterns. It always embarrasses me. I see it as a ritual without the ritual, like a car without a gearbox, but she doesn't seem bothered and we have the odd dance but once we start talking we chat for hours companionably close, not wanting to dance. Talking is more intimate. I don't understand what modern dancing is about, just jigging up and down more or less in time with the music seems daft to me, childish and pointless, and the way Georgie Fame plays doesn't help. The music goes with the drugs, kind of twitchy. It fits the mood somehow.

We talk as if we've saved the words for weeks to pour out in a flood. It's so much better than dancing. It may have to do with the pills but it's not just the speed. She's called Diane and works in her father's shop. It's an insurance agency in Brentwood High Street. She's so like me.

"I sit all day ticking boxes for insurance. Dad does the houses - that's the biggest part of the business. Most of what I do that's not cars is industrial. 'Is there a flat roof or a pitched roof with lead flashing?' 'Is there any inflammable material stored on the site?' 'Are the floors wooden or concrete?' I don't care and it comes out with the customers. I feel like telling them to burn the place then none us would have to mess around filling boring forms to insure it. Mostly you can tell they're dumps and not worth insuring anyway." Unlike me she doesn't get on with her father at all. Whereas I know my father is on my side, she's at daggers drawn with her Dad, largely because he more or less forces her to work in the shop, a bit like a marriage of convenience. She hates being treated that way. Who can blame her?

We've agreed to meet next week. I wanted it to be tomorrow. She did too, but she's got something on already. She was a bit funny about it and she made me feel a bit insecure about seeing her again. I want to see her again. It's important to me. I want to see her a lot but in the week isn't sensible. Dagenham is quite a way from Brentwood and it couldn't be any sooner. I have the car but no full licence. An hour either way on buses in midweek after finishing work isn't realistic. Going to bed on Saturday morning and waking mid-afternoon feeling like 'death on legs' after Friday's speed is more than compensated. But next weekend - and Diane, feels as distant as hot sun on a foggy day in November.

ঌঌঌঌ

60

Getting to Grips With A Real Contract

Monday September 12th 1966 8.12 a.m

The site manager who was due to come on Friday has turned up. I'm told he rang me on Friday but no one gave me the message that he'd be here first thing today. He's with Gallatia at the moment and I have to wait till he's finished before we can get to work sorting out exactly how the job is to be done. I'm sitting 'making work' drawing a coloured plan of all the pipework in the plant. It's a job for life and a complete waste of time so I can afford to be preoccupied with thoughts of the weekend past and the promise of the weekend to come. I can't wait. I can't get the Bachelors crap song *My Diane* out of my head. I'm humming *My Diane*. Soft, tough, dazzling, Diane.

The truth regarding pipes is they're fitted where and when they're needed and drawings are largely theoretical and pointless.

Humming, *My Diane*. again

At last. Here we go. *My Diane*.

Bugger the job.

My Diane.

194

I sit bloody-minded, knowing they're coming to me but I pretend to be absorbed in the crucial work I'm so deeply involved in. I don't know why, perhaps it's catching. Is it Gallatiaitis?

Bugger Gallatia.

Bugger the job.

My Diane. I'm fidgeting.

See you smile.

"This is Mr Charles." Gallatia's introducing the contractors man. He looks alright. Dark hair, youngish, early thirties I guess, generally clean cut but with a largish, slightly lumpy nose. He's a bit taller than me, slim but well built and wearing a smart grey suit, and grey shoes, bit 'ugh', especially the shoes - but smiles easily and looks as though he might enjoy a joke, though I'm learning fast that looks can deceive. Light grey shoes, hmm. 'Wonder what Diane would think of him?'

"Hello. I'm Dave, Dave Ray." We shake hands.

"Hi. John Charles, Not to be confused with either the prince or the footballer. I'll be the site manager."

I think, 'Better to have kept it simple.' He's as sincere as Churchill kissing Stalin,

"If I do my job properly you'll have nothing much to do, eh?" - giving a small forced chuckle. "That's the way we want it, eh, good for everybody?"

My thoughts follow a, 'You scratch my back etc' route.

"No problems and a good result at the finish; no need to tell you I'll be doing my best. With an old building like that you can never tell what you're going to find but I've had a good look around and can't see any major pitfalls, so it's just a case of keep our fingers crossed." Gallatia, losing interest, says, " I'll leave you two to get on with it . Any real difficulties come and see me and we'll sort things out." Turning back to his office.

"Okay, let's go and get started," says John, heading purposefully for the door.

He's carrying a rolled up bundle of drawings and it's clear he's seen the job already because he knows the way, stepping casually across the railway lines, hardly looking for engines, as though he's worked here for years and knows the lines are mostly disused these days. At the Sultzer Plant are two of his men with a Transit van. The double doors to the building entrance are open. I wonder who let them in? They've already brought in big builders' toolboxes and are fitting the hose between a pneumatic drill and mobile compressor.

John lays the master drawing out on top of one of the toolboxes, weighting the corners with a selection of chisels from the jack-hammer carrying case.

"Have you seen these drawings yet?"

"Oh yes and I've read the spec. It seems to me the biggest part of the job is clearing the place out, cutting the hole to the first floor, and fitting the stairs. The thing that bothers me most is the stairs themselves. The drawing shows them in concrete. I don't know anything about working with concrete but casting them in here I'd have thought would be a right performance."

"The plan's not to cast them here but drop them in with a crane. It'll mean cutting a hole in the roof as well but I think that's the cheapest way of doing the job."

I've not even considered doing this. If it had been left to me I'd have fabricated the stairs from steel.

"What about the roof when you've done? It's flat and if you start messing about with it isn't there a chance there'll be leaks?'
I've heard about problems with flat roofs.

"People worry about flat roofs. If they're done properly they'll last as long as a pitched roof. An inch or two of asphalt on six inches of reinforced concrete won't give any problems for years, as long as it's done properly."

"Well, you're the man who knows. If there are leaks it'll be down to your people."

"There'll be no trouble with leaks, believe me."

"George," he calls.

"This is George, he's our charge-hand. How long before the

196

place is cleared d'you think, George?" There are concrete plinths where machines have stood and they'll take some breaking up. There's the hole to cut in the floor too. This concrete is good stuff. I wouldn't like to break it up.

"It depends how we do it. If we just use the drill I'd guess it's going to take a week at least, but there's a quicker way. You need to be a bit careful, but it'd save a lot of hard work."

"Oh what's that?" I enquired, swallowing the hook dangled before me.

"You've got burning gear here, haven't you? If you warm the concrete up." (I guess warm is understatement for several hundred degrees) "and then chuck cold water on it it'll almost break itself up. The only thing is, it spits when you put the torch on it and you need to keep out of the way of the bits coming off. They fly a bit, take your eye out just like that" - snapping his fingers.

"Sort out some gas gear and welders leathers and a mask. We can manage it all right. I've done it before."

I can tell he wants to do it this way as it's obviously easier and quicker, but dangerous, and he's not really qualified to operate gas-cutting gear. John Charles looks sideways at me, eyes wide, eyebrows raised, hands, palm up, outstretched, with a crooked grin, saying, "Don't look at me. It's nothing to do with me."
He's not taking any responsibility. Thoughts of Trevor pass through my mind. It's the sort of thing he'd revel in. He breaks rules the way climbers climb mountains, because they are there.

"I'll think about it," I say.
Charles intervenes.

"It'd help us if we've got some idea how long this is going to take, then I can sort out ordering the crane. I've got to get contractors in for the floors as well. We won't do the floors. Screeding in this sort of set up is best left to specialists. I could do with a word with your electricians too, then we can start to think about how best to lay out the wiring. I'll need to get the plumbing worked out and there'll be ground work involving them, so there's plenty to do."

This is all a bit different to the painters on the crane. These people know what they're about, willing to cut corners where they can, but aiming to do a properly serviceable job, whilst getting the thing moving as quickly as possible.

The compressor has started and we exchange a sideways glance, as George, looking businesslike hefts the drill like a cricketer hefting the bat as he takes the crease.

"Seems like it might be time to get back to your office and a cup of tea," Charles smiles.

"Sounds okay to me." The shattering rattle of the drill echoes and reverberates around the bare concrete buildings, assaulting our ears as we go. At the workshop I lead the way to Rance's office, knocking, stepping inside and standing back to let Charles in ahead of me.

"Frank, this is John Charles. He's the site foreman for the Sultzer Plant conversion job. There's some steel reinforcing that needs burning gear to cut. Any chance of borrowing Trevor for a bit." Rance, glad to see someone else taking responsibility for mad Trevor jumps at the chance to release himself from the niggling worry.

"He's all yours. There's not much on for him at the moment anyway, so yeh, take him. How long do you think you'll need him? Just so I know."

"'Hard to say. There's god knows what reinforcing in that old Sultzer building and we've only just started this morning. If you need him back, just let me know."

"Okay, leave it like that then."
Trevor's usually in the main workshop, because the foremen like to keep an eye on him. I shout, "Hey, Trevor, there's a job that's right up your street. Get a burning set over to the old *Sultzer* Plant and ask for George. He's the contractor's chargehand. He'll tell you what he wants." "So now they've got boys doing foremen's jobs, have they? Who told you you could give me orders."

"I'm just following orders, same as you, and I'm doing you a favour. It'll get you out of here for an hour or two and it's a job that'll suit you right down to the ground."

"It better be good. Dragging a fuckin' burning set all the way to the Sultzer Plant's gonna take three quarters of an hour on its own."

"Ah, stop moaning and do something useful for a change," I laugh. Another of Mother's sayings passes through my mind. 'Hit 'em and laugh, they don't think you mean it'. I'm still in a good mood and can carry off being cheeky as images of Diane still intermittently flit through my head. He's getting his stuff ready. The argument's just a formality.

61

A Proposition?

Wednesday October 19th 1966 10.00a.m

John Charles says, "Might be as well if we keep out of the way for the moment. How d'you fancy taking a look at the staircase at our place. Might be a good idea if we did some checking and made sure everything's okay, don't you think? It's nearly lunchtime and we could get a coffee on the way."

With his face and body language he's indicating that he thinks it's a good idea if we're well out of the way if anything goes wrong with the concrete breaking. I've not told Trevor to do anything other than cut reinforcing steel so what he and George get up to is their responsibility. If anything goes wrong I'm pretty well covered and the lure of some time out is tempting, especially with the possibility of a pleasant half hour over coffee. I smile agreement and nod.

"I'd be interested to see your place and a coffee wouldn't go amiss."

"Right. Follow me and if all goes well things should be moving along nicely when we get back."

The contractor's works is about ten miles away along the A13 and then down a side-road towards the river. John's driving a top of the range car; it's a Ford Zephyr Zodiac. It has an American feel to it, brash two-tone pastel paintwork and white walled tyres, smart by the standards of the time but typical Ford styled - clunky, ugly, with lots of cheap chrome, flashy colours and a smell of plastic. American car design was never good. Ford heaters are the best. The rest is just cheap and cheerful like the tanks they sold us duing the war.

***

European cars have always had better steering and more style than American. Americans think nothing of driving hundreds of miles on straight roads, and their fuel is cheap. With this in mind their cars are made spacious and comfortable, with enormous slobby engines. They ride and steer like boats. The American market has its roots in mass sales - like their tanks - and just like their tanks they're not good for Europe.

The road we're on could be in America. Telegraph poles tick past fast, measuring time laterally, like the punch clock, instead of sensibly, quietly, round a genial, circular clock-face. The scene is unplanned boomtown. We wait at traffic lights; the engine murmurs a deeper countertpoint to the heater hum. Drips skitter down the windows as rainsqualls shake the car. The steady, click thump, click thump, of wipers on the screen is soporific. At the kerbside stands a grease-black eight-by-four bowed plywood sign, corners worn round through daily dragging over broken paving stones. It struggles in showery gusts to escape the tired rope, binding it upright to a telegraph pole. The base is delaminating in oil fluorescent black water where crooked bits of broken slabs stick up from the puddle, dislodged and crushed by the tyres of heavy lorries. Grey, skies, give poorly formed hand-painted letters, in dirt-contaminated white paint, a sadder even tragic aspect as they proclaim 'CAR SPARES CHEEP.' The joke's not intentional, just sad. The smashed slabs meet a dangerous, mackledtogether fence, festooned in tangles of barbed wire, reminiscent of the Somme. Beyond the wire, dead cars piled four high make jagged silhouettes against clouds they all but touch. Accelerating fast, we whip through the gut wrenching ugliness, adding our contribution of fine-sprayed muck thrown up in a hissing roar of spinning tyres, veiling everything in road grime. Flashy, fair ground styled neon signs of truck stops, second-hand car dealers, tyre sales bays and cheap showy new motels all scream at one another across the road. It has the down-market look of a down-town, American film set. A few bedraggled trees survive the ravages of 'progress.' Ford-ugly is overflowing into this wasteland, where sag-faced pubs survive to make pivotal points in rows of dejected pre-war bungalows, refugees from a more healthy time. The whole is infected with Ford-ugly. It's gangrenous, incurable. The only treatment: amputation and incineration.

I feel dislocated, my thoughts distracted and clumsy because the transient nature of this nightmare world impresses on me the irregular, catch as catch can, fleetingness of it all. It's in stark contrast to the solid sameness of the housing estate I pedalled my bike through three hours ago, accentuating the unreality of slipping around on these shiny, red plastic seats with the fug from the heater cutting us off from the cold outside the car. My handle bars transmitted cold to my fingers and the positive push of the pedals against my feet fed an accustomed relaxed and friendly tiredness that at the end of each day keeps me in contact with the reality that the car masks or paralyses, shutting people away from people and the truth of existence in a pernicious, unhealthy way.

John's excited by boot lids and bumpers. He's a gourmet of carbon monoxide. We're chewing fumes while he tries to squeeze us into the exhaust of the car in front. He's careful to check his headlamps are working, flashing to make sure they light up the rear of the vehicle ahead before we climb into its tail pipe. He's a man on the way up and he's out to prove it with his king dick Zephyr Zodiac. His driving technique complements his yuck grey suit and dodgy grey shoes.

Stopping for coffee at a new motel, the place, like the car, is shoddy and over the top. I go to the toilet and sit to find the seat heated, it's not just quietly warmed, it's hot enough to make me junp. I instantly name it 'hot-seat bog'. It nearly shocks the crap out of me, sharpening my senses and awareness of pungent perfumed disinfectant used in an attempt to smother the smell of stale urine reminiscent of the abandoned pavilion at 'Matchy'.

Returning, I find John has bought coffee. It tastes good, though I'm no judge. I've had some experience of coffee bars, but not much. My wages don't run to that sort of thing and I don't care, there are more interesting things to think about than drinking trendy coffee in kitsch motels.

The song's still swirling inside my mind 'Smile Diane'.
I wonder what she's thinking. I'll tell her about the hot toilet seat. That'll make her laugh. John asks if I want anything to eat. I look at him, saying,

"Money?"

"Oh don't worry about that, I get an expense account."

"Lucky you, they don't even let me out. I haven't clocked out and I should have. It feels odd being out like this and still an apprentice. They could sack me for it. I should have asked permission."

Warning bells are ringing. Something's not right. Charles is smiling and the way he carries himself indicates we're here for more than coffee and some time skiving off the job. He knows I'm growing wary. That's good - all senses are on triple time.

"You can have something to eat if you want," He's trying to put me at ease.

"I think I'd better drink this, go and see your place, and get back. If my Mum knew I'd not bothered with her sandwiches I'd more than get it in the neck."

"Don't worry, Mr Gallatia knows you're with me. He's asked me to have a word. We do quite a bit together and he's asked me to talk to you. He thinks you've got off on the wrong foot with him.

He's asked me to show you this." I'm more than wary now. What the hell's this? What are they cooking up now?

Ferreting in his brief case he slips out a copy of the *Ford Bulletin,* a propaganda broadsheet the company pushes around the factory. He pokes it at me like some old bag from the Sally Army, in a pub, demanding money with menaces till you've parted with some cash for *War Cry.* Fat chance he's got - shoving it at me like that. I want to tell him to fuck off out of my space. That'd be as subtle as him. He's as blunt as a dredger dumping mud in a barge. Swallowing my disgust, I look. It's dated August 8, 1962 - four years old. I'm mystified. He's pointing, with the exaggerated animation of someone dumb, to an article written by the leader of the Amalgamated Engineering Union, a man called Bill Carron, who, from his photo, could be Slippery Lips' brother, dieting, with a leer that he's practised watching sleazy strip shows instead of Slippery's clandestine porn mags. John's working hard to appear reasonable and unbiased and failing dismally as he says, "Have a read and tell me what you think."

The article argues, that government policy has evolved, so the role of the unions has changed. These are quotes 'Many of the old tasks which confronted the pioneers of the union movement have been completed, or very nearly so.' - 'Management has adopted a completely new approach because the interests of working men and management have converged.' - 'The reason for this managerial heart-change is not hard to find. Markets are necessary for our products. The manufacturing employer has to fight for individual survival that is conditional upon the peace and security in his workshops and establishments. It's that simple!' Essentially the war is over. The Empire's gone and with it gunboat diplomacy. 'Old attitudes of outright militancy no longer have a place. - The motives of those who demonstrate such militancy spring from attempts to replace the system of government that we have in the United Kingdom with one that has been repeatedly rejected in elections by an overwhelming majority of opinion.' 'Higher average wages - mean - improved living standards. The conscientious trades unionist should examine very carefully any proposed idea or action before committing himself.'

In short don't strike or listen to the reds because your job's on the line.

It's made to sound all carrot, you don't get to the whip till the last line but it's there all right.

I've talked to Gilley and read a bit of Keynes, and realise that this article is part of the work of implementing Keynsian ideas. From Gallatia's point of view they're trying to rescue me from the clutches of Gilley, the reds and the shop stewards committee that are running the unofficial union and strikes; but I have nothing to do with them. I just do what seems right to me. I like Gilley and I like Charles less and less. Those dodgy grey shoes say more about what's going on in his head than on his feet. I certainly don't like Gallatia. As for managerial heart-changes, comedy belongs in the theatre, and purjury's a crime. I haven't forgotten Fred's smashed body. This article shows Gilley is right when he says the official union leaders are joining the management with a view to playing the game their way. I understand that constant growth is the means by which working people are now to be controlled. The real question is whether I think this is good or bad, and there's no simple answer. 'They' are intending to use a short-term solution. The carrot of an ever-growing wage packet rather than repression that's likely to bring about civil strife and an outcome similar to that in Russia.

I wouldn't trust Gallatia with the greasy dirt under my finger nails. If this little episode does anything, it'll push me towards bright scarlet hammers and sickles because of the way Gallatia has presented his position, but I'm beginning to get to grips with their 'never commit yourself to anything then no one can ever call you a liar' version of politics, and answer non- committally.

"Well Carron's got a point of view and so have the shop stewards, but most important of all, all sides need to act honestly and it seems to me that money's not everything. Everyone should look further than simply the pound in their pocket. They set me working in crownwheels and pinions where I could earn loads of money, but it drove me mad. No-one wants to work there because it drives everyone mad. Something needs to be done about that, and outside of that altogether. Do we need all these bloody cars anyway? Look at that shitty mess out there." I nod towards the road. "There was a bloke I was working with who got killed over a year ago. It needn't have happened. His wife's still not had a penny from the Company and she's got kids to bring up. It's not right. What's going to happen about that?"

I don't mention that I helped pull Fred out of the river, how awful his face looked and how it's bothered me ever since and caused me to think. I don't want to be noncommittal. I want to tell him to put his balls in a mincer and turn the handle to see if it hurts, or better still go and try working in crownwheels and imagine that's the be-all and end-all of his future, and see how he feels then.

"Yeh, all that's all very well, but Mr Gallatia thinks you've got talent. He thinks you've got what it takes to make management, and he wants you on board but he reckons you need to think carefully about your attitude. What Carron's saying in that article is that we all need to pull together. I'll leave it at that but Mr Gallatia's told me about you and you need to think hard about what you're doing. In the end it's up to you, but if I was you I'd be careful, you only get so many chances and this is a real chance. Anyway that said we better get on with it and go and see how these steps are coming on."

I find out later from Brown the assistant shop steward that Charles is somehow related to Gallatia, his son-in-law or something. More bloody wheels within wheels. I'm beginning to be suspicious of everybody now, and wonder how Brown knows about their relationship. Is it wheels within wheels within wheels? Is Brown a really devious bastard spying for Gallatia with a foot in both camps. He was more than a bit interested in my records for the sinter pallet bearings. Just because you're paranoid it doesn't mean they're not after you. It seems to me that Gallatia is offering the same thing as Slippery Lips, wage slavery or a slave overseer's job even. If I toe his line I'll be selling my soul for silver and he'll hold my job over me like a sword of Damocles.

205

It's all rolling around in my head like a lead ball squeezing other thoughts out of its path; even pushing out comforting thoughts of Diane. The more I think about it, the less I like it. In the end it amounts to making cars, to get to work in cars, to make more cars, what a stupid idea. The chairman of General Motors is even quoted as saying 'My ideal car falls apart the day the warranty runs out.' Do I want to be part of that? I'd prefer they just hung me and got the thing done rather than keep shoving their tortuous blackmailing schemes under my nose.

62

'On my Terms'

Without consciously thinking about it I slip into a kind of semi-automatic, zombie state, doing my job, aware that my attitude will not - cannot - change. In the past I felt like an outsider and it worried me; I wanted to fit in. Now the opposite is true. I have no intention of fitting in. All I want is escape. I belong to me and, all being well, Diane, for better or worse. Without being thoroughly aware of what I'm doing, I start to consider everything I do at work with a critical eye as to whether I'm comfortable with it. I'll finish the apprenticeship, but on my terms, while drawing succour from thoughts of Diane. I'll do my job to the best of my ability, without compromising my conscience. I'll do nothing I think she might not approve of. I don't mind polishing boots, but I'll not lick them. If I'm to dance, it will be with Diane, not as a marionette tethered to strings pulled hither and yon by Fords. I'll not let the foul place taint me any more than it has already.

We carry on to the plant where John Charles works. It seems well run, bland, efficient and coated with a light grey mantle of cement dust. It's mainly devoted to casting concrete in custom-made moulds. The steps for our job aren't ready, but the mould is complete so the major part of the work has been done. There's a big concrete mixing plant, a great bare shed, a lot of plywood moulds, an office and not a lot else. The idea lurks in my mind that Charles has brought me here as a pretext for working as middle-man between Gallatia and me. Why the hell Gallatia needs to convey his messages through Charles, I'll never know.

We drive back to Fords and make our way to the Sultzer Plant. Trevor is on the first floor with the burning gear. I don't want to know how the equipment got up there, but it's quite clear that he's having the time of his life breaking rules and concrete. He's hopping around like a sparrow on speed.

"Fuckin' great, didn't know how good an acetylene torch was for breaking concrete. I've thought about workin' on demolition but it always looked as though it might be fuckin' harder than welding, but if you could do this all the time it'd be a lot better. Me and George are getting on like a house on fire, eh George?"

George, looking uncomfortable, shifting his weight from foot to foot, has already sensed there's something not quite right about Terry. and says, "We're doing all right but we've got to be careful' - casting a doubtful look at Terry. "It is speeding the job up though. At this rate we should be a week ahead of schedule by the end of the week, and that never happens, so we can all be pleased."

Charles says "I'll get on my way. There's nothing much here for me to do but I'll sort out the crane for the stairs for next Tuesday. The stairs are the big job and once they're finished we can start thinking about services. Then quietly he said to me "Think about that Carron article; it could make your future. I'll call you tomorrow."

The job goes ahead and with the dubious talents of Terry, progress is faster than anticipated. His services are no longer needed by Thursday morning. George is already thinking in terms of services. Water and electricity need laying on. The necessary groundwork is well under way and Charles has ordered the crane for Monday. On my

207

way back to the office curiosity gets the better of me and I slip up to Stan's and my old workshop on the top floor of the sinter plant. The red dust is coating everything again now the air conditioner is turned off. I'm annoyed that the work we did to sort the place out is going to waste, but I'm elated to note that the cupboard I mentioned to Gerrard has been cleared and the lock is gone. It looks as though the records I kept have an importance I don't fully understand, but I've got an idea. Lucky I kept copies.

৵৵৵৯৯

63

I Feel like a king

Friday September 16th 1966 5.58 p.m

I'm at a coffee shop in Romford that's part of Harrison Gibson, a big furniture store that everybody knows because it has just been rebuilt after a huge fire and is one of the fanciest shops in East London. I'm early but arrive only seconds before Diane. I'm pleased she's early, but for a couple of minutes I'm a bit tentative and clumsy because we've not met this way before. She looks great.

Too classy for me, but as soon as we're sitting together we're chatting sixteen to the dozen, as though we've known one another since we were kids.

She's turning heads. She's wearing brown. Nobody wears brown at the moment, everything's in primary colours or black and white. It's a suit cut to be a bit more shapely than a mod suit. There's a woman in Romford making a fortune churning out 'Mod' two piece suits for girls that are smart but what Diane's wearing is in a different league. It's a bit lighter colour than the soft centre of a coffee cream, with a bold inch and a half wide, dark chocolate stripe that runs diagonally from shoulder to hip that's repeated in the skirt. The stripes are sewn in. It must have been a devil to make and it's well done. Describing cloth properly is girl's business. The best I can manage is lightweight gabardine and the stripe in some kind of velvet. Looking at it from an engineering point of view, I think mixing the materials that way would cause problems because the different natures of the cloth would make the thing hang wrong, but it works, so the maker's got a natural feeling for the cloth she works with. That makes what she's done art.

Under the jacket a couple of inches below the throat is a quarter of an inch of dark chocolate piping at the edge of a soft woollen jumper the same colour as the suit. It's like a necklace. The jumper looks so soft as to make me want to stroke it. It's almost as touchable as her skin. I half shake my head to push away images that stop me concentrating. The colour matches the suit beautifully and it sets off her skin just right, while the stripe sets off her hair. She looks edible like something off a wedding cake. It might be over the top but she can get away with it because all the 'Mod' girls look smart. My nose too often sends messages I'd rather not get but this one I can't get enough of - good, good, good. I linger with a kiss to give my nose as well as the rest of me the full benefit, and squeeze her hand. I can't believe she's with me. Simply touching her is pure pleasure. I feel honoured. It would be pathetic if it weren't so good.

We wander around the town for a while, enjoying holding hands and being silly experimenting with keeping in step and laughing like kids trying to miss the joins in the paving stones. It seems even sillier with her dressed the way she is. But it's not just silly, it's the way dancing should be, dead sexy but not crude. We decide on a film but it's a waste of time, we want to talk and we're whispering. People are shushing us. We leave to find somewhere quiet and warm. The only place that suits is a posh hotel. Normally if I went into a place like this there'd be some kind of bouncer eyeing me up, wondering whether to give me the big E. They're hardly aware of me, with Diane in that suit - they almost simper. We're comfortable and just chat. I feel like a king.

I tell her about the hot-seat bog and we giggle. She tells me about how she feels chained to the insurance agency and how she's interested in art and wants to do dress design. I say "I think the suit is great and you should be doing it." 'I only finished the lining last night." She shows me the marks where the skin of her index finger has been marked by the blunt end of the needle. I enjoy myself, half joking, stroking it and offering sympathy. She takes it away laughing at me before I can kiss it but then she turns over the hem of her skirt to show me the hand-stitched lining. I say "Stop it or I'll bite your leg." She laughs pushing me away saying "Get off." She's having fun winding me up but then calls a halt and gets serious, sketching some of her ideas on scraps of paper. I go into the tales of asking David Hockney about art and missing the job at the advertising agency.

She asks "Couldn't you get a job in the design department at Fords ?" I tell her "I'm nowhere near qualified enough for it and I'm not sure I'd want it. Look at the Anglia with those stupid peaks over the lamps. They call them a design feature; they reduce the efficiency of the car and they look awful. They haven't got designers. They've got some sort of devotees of the god of ugly or something. Everything about the place is ugly. If you tried to create ugly for an exercise you couldn't do it better than them, They're wizards of ugly. Do you know before the First World War there were already ten million cars in America, but in England there were only a few thousands. The Model 'T' was made as cheaply and as simply as possible so it was functional and that's all. It's a good design as a machine, if you're not interested in aesthetics. It works and there's no more to say. That's what the factory's like. It's just the bare minimum to do the job. So what do we get? Cheap and ugly. It must be one of the ugliest places on earth. It goes with the way they think. Money, money, money. Cars here are status symbols, the same as in America, but here the fat cats are more subtle. Design is more understated but more sensual and sexy. Americans think 'If you've got it, you should flaunt it' so everything they make is either big or flashy."

"Here the rich look down at us dead snotty and their cars are more or less hand made. They're like your suit, made by people like you with real flair, not just smashed out in some dreary factory - bomp, bomp, bomp." She kissed me. She knew I wasn't saying it to flatter her. I was on my hobby horse now and even the kiss didn't stop me.

"Our cars are made to look a bit old fashioned. I think it's 'cos it reminds the fat cats of the days when they had our mums and dads running around like slaves. We're just getting a super compromise sorted out when our car industry is going down the pan. The Mini and 'E' Type are some of the best designs ever. We're a failure in a way, but from a different point of view, we're doing great. Do we want to knock ourselves out churning out cars when we can have a bit of fun? There's a sort of irony about it. The Mini and 'E' Type go with fun, and Steed, Mrs Peel and the Avengers, and style, but making the cars is drudgery - the exact opposite it's ... what's the word? A paradox. My Mum and Dad have hardly had a life with the depression and rationing and the war."

Diane says, "My Mum and Dad are the same. He started walking the streets and drumming up trade by door knocking and he never lets us forget it. He lives and dies for the business, but he never has time to spend any of the money and he kind of worships money. Mum's only got to say there's more to life than money and he goes mad. He's all right really but the business has become too much a part of him; it's more or less an obsession. Everything he does he regards almost as part of the business. If we go on holiday it'll be where there's an insurance convention or something like that. There's got to be more to life than insurance but if I said that to my Dad he'd go crackers."

Thoughts of fun lead me to ask. "Have you heard of a group called the Rolling Stones? I know a few people who've seen them. Everyone says they're really good and they're on at a hall over Smart Western at Dalston Junction soon. Allie and Alastair are going. D'you want to? You'll kill 'em if you wear that suit."

"The Stones? Great. When?"

"It's the Saturday after next. I'll see if I can still get tickets."

We part early. She has to work in the shop tomorrow morning.

"You're the only one who hasn't said I'm daft for wanting to be a dress designer and not laughed at me," she says giving me a real kiss as I take her hand in both mine and shiver with the hair on my neck standing up. We have to separate early to catch our buses, but the hug and kiss as we part is so disturbing I have to stop quickly, I'm almost beside myself. I feel I might crush her I so want to squeeze her close.

"You make my toes curl up," she says,

"That's nothing compared to what you do to me" - not just looking at my feet.

She smacks my hand playfully, coy and laughing, a little confused, complimented but at the same time reserved at what could be read as my boldness. She gives me the benefit of the doubt though and we arrange to meet again the following Friday in the same place. We're greedy for each other's company.

64

Checking the Records

It's a long Saturday. Diane's either in the back of my mind or dominating my thoughts. I have a driving lesson with Bernie from the by-products on Sunday. That helps to pass the time. When we finish, I ask him if he can wangle me some overtime when the office staff are not around. "Why? What for? Are you skint or something?"

"Gallatia's asked for the original records I kept to show that the greasing machine Stan and me fitted in the sinter plant saved enough cash to merit a full payout on the suggestion scheme. The other day he got Shorty to ask me again. I told Gallatia I'd left the stuff locked in a cupboard in our office on the top floor of the plant and I went up there yesterday to see if the cupboard was still locked and the lock was gone and it was empty. They've emptied the whole place and the maintenance is falling apart already. I went with Gilley to a union meeting a week ago and I took the records with me. I thought the union might do something. Some hope – bloody waste of time. But Browny, Banks' mate, the assistant steward, went through 'em like they were the Dead Sea Scrolls and he was going to walk off with 'em. I stopped him and he made out it was absent mindedness but I could see he was disappointed and didn't want to give 'em back. I think he's a stool pigeon for Gallatia. Yesterday - low and behold - funny old Gerrard who doesn't say a word to anybody comes over to me and starts chatting as if we were old mates, and what's he interested in? Bernie nods, eyes wide, smiling "Yeh the records I kept of the sinter plant bearings. What I want to do is get into Gerrard's files and see how the requisition records match up to the records I kept. I think someone's been fiddling and I think Gallatia knows. I think Gerrard knows too and I think that's why the poor bastard works here and spends four hours a day travelling to work in this shithole. I think Gallatia daren't pay out on our suggestion because it'd show up the fiddle, and he's up to his neck in it."

Bernie's shaking his head and his face has slowly been cracking into a smile as wide as a bank robbers' in the vault at Fort Knox. "Hwoo - If that's right, you'll have the bastard by the short and curlies. It could be better than getting the suggestion. I'll bet he's shitting bricks. I like it. - I like it. Overtime? I'll tell you what I'll do. I'll tell Rancy the submersible pump for the cooling tower is playing up. It's a shitty job but you've worked on it before and we'll get Stan in on it. We'll tell 'em we need him to drive the fork truck, that way we'll get a whole weekend so the office'll be all yours for as long as you want."

At work, things are going well. Cutting the hole in the roof turns out to be quite easy. The roof is made of hollow bricks with a coating of asphalt about an inch thick that can easily be re-melted and replaced. By the end of the day the crane is gone and the stairs are in place. There's still a lot to do; lots of final fixing and finishing, but the basic structural work is done. Charles is obviously pleased, saying, "There aren't many new builds that go as well as this. 'To fail to prepare is to prepare to fail, eh." (I bet he doesn't know he's quoting Benjamin Franklin) "'And I've got to hand it to you, Dave, the preparation couldn't have been better."

He's a great one for trite, go getting, American quotations like 'When the going gets tough, the tough get going.' I read recently about 'Speedy Taylor' who was obsessed with efficiency and turned rounders into baseball because it was more efficient. Charles would be happy with that and he and Diane's Dad would get on fine. I have a problem with it. Quality is important to me and locker rooms are simply functional - and the same applies to insurance. Charles is failing to acknowledge art, beauty and emotion. I think 'Man lives not by bread alone' money's not everything. It seems likely that Diane's Dad's the same as Charles.

Despite feeling that way about Charles, I went home feeling good, because the work had gone so well. I didn't get a chance to talk to Freddy or Stan. I got second in the clock queue. We always race, but Diane gives me an added incentive.

***

At home Mum's happy for me, and smiling with a wide eyed knowing nod, says, "You're early. Got a new admirer, you have, she phoned this morning. Diane, she sounded really nice on the phone. She said not to phone her though, but she'll meet you at Harrison Gibson's in Romford at six on Friday. She said she'd ring again to make sure that's okay. She said you can't phone anytime. Haven't they got a phone? She seemed a bit cagey. Is there something going on? I said she could phone here anytime and you were nearly always in after six,but she said it's a bit difficult. I can't see why. She sounds nice though. Where did you meet her? What's she like? You can bring her here anytime you know. I can always fit another one in. We might not be posh but there's always good food on the table."

Mum is a bit worried about girls and me. She thinks I'm too shy and she doesn't think it's healthy for me to sit around reading as much as I do. More than once she's tried a bit of match-making with one or other of our neighbour's daughters who is said to have shown an interest. What she doesn't realise is that, although shyness may play a part, I really am not interested. I think I must be a romantic or something. I didn't know what I was looking for, but I know I've found it all right. Diane is the one. Hurry up Friday. Christmas is a washout compared to Diane.

"I only met her a fortnight ago. You'll like her," I tell Mum. "She makes her own clothes and she's not half good at it."

"Hmm, that's good. When are you going to bring her home?"

"Don't know. She lives at Brentwood and it's a bit of a long way." I don't say too much. I don't know how things are going to turn out and I don't want to make a fool of myself. I still blush easily.

***

Things are easy at work now. Everything is details and lots of annoying niggles. Getting the fittings we need when we need them is the biggest problem. Two hundred lockers arrive that are the wrong size because the suppliers have run out of the right ones. Mrs Short has started to half simper at me; even she senses something's going on. The lockers go back and I have to find a different supplier who can get what we want. I spend a couple of frustrating days phoning around before arriving at a half reasonable result. Charles's team are good, turning up on time and doing their work conscientiously. I'm not really needed most of the time and keep out of the way, visiting Freddy in the by-products and generally wandering around killing time. It's the last thing I need. I want something to occupy my mind, otherwise I spend all my time thinking of Diane - just hanging around agonising waiting for the weekend. Charles comes frequently to keep his eye on things, but the truth is there are more chiefs than are needed and I have the feeling that some of the Indians resent me. Although they're not *Ford* men, it's obvious that I'm little more than a boy and they are good at their jobs. I'm feeling a fraud so I get my overalls on and start to get involved with the work, doing some of the labouring and general running around. Mrs Short's confused and flickers and simpers and gives me snotty looks by turns. The praying and bowing is becoming a habit. I told her I was thinking of becoming a Buddhist the other day and she's getting a bit nervous when she's near me. It's probably no bad thing. It'll stop her talking out of turn when even she realises she's either been left behind, ribbed something rotten, or she's watching me go as mad as half the rest of the people who work here.

65

Pleasure Together & Common Interests

Friday September 23rd 1966 5.57p.m

I've got the tickets to see the Rolling Stones. One of the first things I do when I meet Diane is show them to her. She laughs saying "Their music's better for dancing to. I might make you dance more when we see them and we'll be able to get home on Friday night without taking pills. My Dad's getting funny about me getting in in the morning. I've been telling him I've been staying at Louise's but he's getting

216

suspicious and I've been having to take another pill to keep going on Saturday mornings because he wants me working in the shop and without the pill I'm 'coming down' and can't do it. Then it takes me the rest of the week to get over it. I'm shattered all week. Then if I go out again the following week it starts all over again and I can't keep it up."

So we take it easy and go to the quiet bar again, walking slowly and taking a long way around. The nights are drawing in and it gives me a chance to hold her close. She has her arm around me and I get the feeling she likes it as much as me and I want to walk for hours with her near me. We don't need, even want, to talk. Just being together is enough.

In the bar we chat. She looks good. She's wearing a short coat and simple dress this week. She knows about clothes and everything she wears works together like the parts of a neat machine and she still looks great. We get around to talking about books. She's a girl and likes *Pride and Prejudice* and *Wuthering Heights* but she's keen on *The Ragged Trousered Philanthropists* too and she likes *The Scarlet Pimpernel* and *Campbell's Kingdom* which surprises me. The main thing is she likes books and not just trashy stuff. She moves onto music (She's more interested in music than me) and says "At The Flamingo West Indian music is being mixed with European, and it's new and really good. Motown is typical American and sounds manufactured. It comes from Detroit and it's like your cars. It's sort of thin and weak."

"Is Motown called that because that's where they make cars in America?" I ask.

"I don't know but it might be. It feels as though it's a bit kind of whiney - sort of production liney. The singers sound as though they're doing a job, almost following a formula. Doing what they're told, for money. Long John Baldry and Georgie Fame are more real and fit with what's going on here. They're not faked up by salesmen but really feel what they're doing when they're playing. I think the Rolling Stones are even better and cos' they're more or less local they know how we feel. The Beatles are better still and they're good looking too."

I give her an offended look, laughing and saying "Yeah, they're all right I suppose" Laughing back provocatively she says "Mick Jagger is good but he's not good looking. England is the place to be though. America's getting left behind." I know exactly what she means. It's almost as though we can read each other's minds. We've talked so much and we're so much alike I don't even want to talk any more. I feel drained in a good way and relaxed I just want to be close to her and get used to feeling her near me. We've got to part early to catch our buses, but we're going to meet tomorrow, even though her Dad won't like not having her in the shop.

***

Saturday September 24th 1966 9.21a.m

The market is just opening and we potter aimlessly; as the market-men set up their stalls; we're enjoying simply being together. I tell her, "I know the man selling the 'miracle' furniture polish. He's got a stooge in the crowd. What he's selling is mostly vinegar and water. It works by taking off old wax polish and if you keep using it, it'll take off the French polish as well. He says he doesn't think it's wrong because what the punters pay for is the show. If you went to a show half as good in the West End you'd pay twice as much. I'm not sure it's right, but you have to admit he's got a point. My Mum's Dad comes from didiquois people, sort of gypsies, that's how I know some of them. Selling like that is a traditional part of the way they make a living. It makes the life of the audience a bit more fun, a bit less humdrum and monotonous."
Diane says,

"I suppose it's a bit like selling insurance, except that's the opposite when it comes to fun. We're sort of selling a silver lining rather than sunshine."

At lunchtime we buy fish and chips and take them to the park.

I'm not easy to live with. I'm funny about the way people eat. There's nothing worse than seeing food churning around in a mouth like a washing machine and words muffled by a mouthful of food. I eat slowly, partly because I don't want to subject anyone else to a view of half chewed food. She goes as slowly as me and is one of the few people I've met who does it just right. I've just become aware of her straight regular teeth. In my eyes she's growing more and more perfect. We're both slow, and without being aware are observing one another in a new intimate situation, and are smiling, happy and pleased at the sight. I make her a clothes peg from a stick of willow and a strip of tin from an old can with my penknife so she knows I wasn't joking about the gypsy thing. She laughs, shakes her head in disbelief and tells me I'm mad... but she keeps it.

In the afternoon it starts to drizzle and we meander around the big stores then to the quiet bar again. We're looking at the way it's decorated. Laughing, I say, "It's not sure if it's staid, thirties, middle class, middle England or half baked Italian palace. The chandeliers are crazy. I wonder who put it together. It's a shambles isn't it? I suppose it'd work in a Disney dream."

Diane's getting high-brow, saying "Good design is emotional. Beauty and elegance are felt as well as created. It goes with a state of mind." We're striking off each other - I say "The American state of mind is crude and ugly, thoughtless and unimaginative and it comes out in its cars. They're ugly because the state of mind of their makers is ugly and the ugliness filters through to Fords in England."

She laughs saying "Anyone would think you've got it in for Fords."

"Too right," I say, hardly laughing, "I'm more than a bit biased, but then there are reasons. A while ago I was working on a job about a hundred feet up. A bloke I was with had told me that before he came to work he'd had letters saying he'd finished paying for his car and his daughter had got seven 'O' Levels. At eleven o clock that day he was killed. He fell a hundred feet into the river and I followed his body as it was washed along by the tide and helped to get him out.

It was ever so cold and he looked smashed up, cold and dead. I don't know why, but I touched him. I touched his forehead and it was like wax, harder and colder than proper skin, even though he was wet and he looked terrible."

She can tell I'm getting upset and jokes to break the tension. "Thank god we didn't sell insurance on the crane. My Dad'ud be heart-broken."

I smile and go into detail about John Charles; how his car's flashy and in poor taste and he wears anti-styled grey shoes, saying, "There's something about Fords. All the people who have anything to do with running it haven't joined with England and the swinging sixties thing. They all belong to America, where the almighty dollar is still king. Really they're all about greed. Here in England it seems to me that even the middle classes are wondering whether the Empire was worth the bother, and people working in Fords haven't cottoned on yet. Orwell's *1984* has made us a bit thoughtful and imaginative and ordinary people want a bit more say."

She knows what I'm getting at, but she sees it in terms of music saying, "Elvis is being left behind and the Beatles and Stones are taking over. The sixties are swinging; everything's getting freer, and you needn't think it has anything to do with you, but contraception's changing things. Have you seen that Swedish advert for Durex. It's a man's thing wriggling into a Durex." She's blushing and laughing but she's said it. "Our England is ever so different from our mums and dads."

We're both a bit embarrassed but determined to brazen it out and we squeeze hands, giggling together. I tell her "I've not seen it" and get highbrow again to cover my embarrassment "Even in the American South, slavery's really being abolished and they're getting real democracy for black people. Have you heard the Martin Luther King speech?" She replies, "Have you read *Cannery Row*? In that, Hazel the negro is more or less an idiot. It makes you wonder about Steinbeck. It's a nice fun book but it's out of date already."

"I hadn't thought about that but I've read it and liked it, but

220

you're right. I've been reading a book called *On The Road* by a hippy called Jack Kerouak. He just gets up and walks away. It's a bit 'way out' with Buddhism and things but makes me feel like picking up sticks and clearing off. If only we could really do it. Would you fancy that, just clear off. Be terrific if we had spare cash."

"Hmm, sounds lovely, all sunshine and sandy beaches but it rains for people like us. It's not for us. Never mind - We'll go and see the Stones next week," she says, giving me a little kiss. Then it's dreamy walking, luscious squeezes, silly chatter and long lingering kisses in the dark by the park gates as we wait for last buses.

***

Considering I'd overseen just two simple contracts before, one of which no sooner started than it stopped, Charles's praise was praise indeed. The work continued to forge ahead well inside the scheduled time, and finished a fortnight earlier than was projected. There was a small official opening and some of the blokes complimented me on the job, pleased with their new showers and locker room.

Charles invited me to a celebration at a smart hotel at Hainault.

"Our boss is really happy with the way it went and he's made extra out of it because we got finished early. It'll start Friday lunchtime. Bring your girl. He can be a bastard when things go wrong but he knows how to celebrate when they go right. You'll enjoy it."

66

Sublime to Ridiculous

Saturday October 1st 7.31p.m 1966

I've just met Diane; we're at Dalston at the station. I came with Allie and his girl and Alastair. Allie and his girl went 'Oooooh' when, on the platform, we gave one another a serious hello kiss and cuddle that would have lasted a lot longer if we'd been alone.

Out in the street it's scruffy, run down, littered, old style East End, built with sooty yellow diarrhoea coloured bricks and streets too narrow for the traffic. It's dominated by the railway, and the clank, clatter and squeal of passing trucks and carriages is almost constant. The dance hall's got an even rougher atmosphere than The Flamingo where violence runs as an undercurrent and adds an edge to the excitement. Here there's something in the air a bit too exciting, more overtly threatening. We've got our tickets; we're committed.

Allie's girl's called Barbara. She's small, with eyes to match and she's tried to compensate with mascara, so her lashes look like chimney sweep's brushes. She's very 'Mod,' with dark hair cut in a bob that ends at points, curling slightly under her jaw. She's wearing soft, white calf-high boots and a dress with alternating black and white squares, starting big at the hem that's around mid thigh with the squares growing smaller as they go upwards. I've an idea she might have shop lifted it in the West End. To get a pattern like that couldn't be cheap and I've heard tales that some of the girls try on several dresses and walk out of the shop wearing the one they went in with and another underneath. Barbara's a lively little 'bird', maybe a bit too lively if she has pinched the dress. Allie's better with girls than me in a way, but some of the girls he finds, I'm not too comfortable with. They often have heads full of cotton wool. Barbara's not like that. She's more the other way, a bit too sharp-edged and knowing for my taste.

The hall's crowded and a lot of people are outside still trying to get in. There's hardly room to dance but the Stones are good. Jagger's a showman. There's something about the way he claps his hands over his head, dancing as he sings. It's cool, with just a hint of menace. He could look a twerp but he carries it off with style in a way that fits the mood of the hour. Diane's not wearing the classy two piece suit, just a simple dress again, but she looks better than Barbara, even without my bias. She's come with a coat as well. It's smart and well cut, shorter than her dress. That's not long. Dress and coat have style. Barbara's got a cardigan. I doubt she shoplifted that.

Alastair's away with the birds. He's been popping pills for a week. He's going off the rails. I don't want too much to do with him. Allie told me they had to carry him onto the train last week. I don't want to get involved with that. I'm trying to dance with Diane but there are just too many people. We're crowded so tight we're just moving together with the music like an oil spill on the beach. I like being with Diane but this place I can do without. The music's loud and good but the atmosphere's not. There's no bar and it's too hot. The ceiling's too low and it makes the place oppressive. Some people have a nose for fancy wine. I developed an understanding of mobs and their moods at school. The menace that goes with Mick Jagger's songs is being transmitted to the dancers, whose frustration at the crush is ready to boil over. "D'you fancy a drink?" I have to yell to make her hear. She nods. She looks uneasy. She feels it too. We slowly nudge our way to the door, where heavies are shouting "Go out and you'll not get back. No pass outs." I look hopefully at Diane. She nods.

We find a pub not far from the hall. It's the sort of place that might serve jellied eels and mild ale that tastes like burnt sacks and is as strong as wet bog roll, but we're hot and it's cold in the street. Inside it's crowded. There are some old blokes, regulars who look as though they've grown into their seats around the walls, with arms that make regular movements to their pints like slow cuckoos popping out of clocks. Then there are the overflow from the dance, some of them are chancey looking characters. I guide Diane to the end of the bar where it's relatively quiet, but hard to get served. There's a jukebox playing some old dear's sentimental, Irish stuff. The pub's an odd mixture, mostly threadbare carpet, old mahogany, and Victorian, but a couple of doors have been 'flushed' with hardboard and painted nicotine stained white so the décor matches the clientele, with an incongruous mixture of tainted modern and old. Diane only wants orange juice, and she's got a seat next to an old geezer who can't get used to the idea he's old and a bit of a wreck like the pub. He's chatting her up as though he's twenty. She's laughing, enjoying the attention, and she's got us a seat. I squeeze in so that Diane's sandwiched between us. She's enjoying herself, giving the old fella' his best night for months.

We're just working towards our second when Allie arrives with Barbara. They're both looking chalky faced enough to stand out and Allie's suit is dirtied down one side. Barbara's half supporting him. Seeing us, they move in our direction. Hushed eyes follow as they make their way across the room. Barbara says "Get us a drink - a vodka and lime." I glance at Allie. "Just half for me; half of bitter."

"What happened?"

"Two guys pushed up to us and one of 'em thumped me. I didn't know what was going on. I was surprised and went down. I half fell over. I wasn't expecting it. And the other bastard kicked me. It was lucky it was so crowded neither of 'em really had enough room to get a good swing. They just hit me for no reason and disappeared. The bouncers got to us while I was still on the floor and chucked us out."

Diane's standing now and the old guy's spreading himself out, looking disgruntled because Allie and Barbara are taking our seats. I get more drinks. "How do you feel?" I ask Allie.

"I'm not too bad; it was just the surprise that got me. It was just so unexpected.' Barbara's drink is already gone and I've not taken a mouthful of mine. Diane's still got most of her orange. Now Allie's got a drink and is sitting down. He's sorting himself out.

"You okay?"

"Yeah, it was the shock more than anything. What are we going to do?" I think he's speeding. He's not out of it like Alastair but getting buzzy. Diane blows it.

"We can go back to mine if you want. It's not ten yet and my Mum and Dad won't be back till late."

"Where is it?" from Barbara, whose eyes are beginning to look like coal holes. She's had a pill or two as well.

"It's Brentwood, but it doesn't take long on the train."

And that's that; we all end up on a train to Brentwood. We even have the misfortune to pick up Alastair and a 'bird' he's got in tow. She's in a bigger state than him. I'm not sure they can even see one another properly and getting them to talk sense is a non-starter. By midnight Diane's trying to throw us out but we've bought some drinks and are just getting settled. Barbara's making a fuss of Allie, Alastair and his girl are sitting next to one another twitching and babbling nonsense, and Diane and me are spending our time trying to coax them to leave. I want go before the parents arrive but I can't leave Diane to sort the others out. The situation isn't ideal when Diane's Mum and Dad arrive. It's just before one o' clock. It doesn't seem as though we've been here more than a few minutes and the truth is we've hardly had time to do any harm. As far as I know we've not even spilt a drink. Mr Gallagher, Diane's dad, is going berserk. I could understand it if we're having an orgy or lighting a campfire in the middle of the sitting room but we're all semi comatose especially Alastair and his 'bird.' There are only six of us including Diane so the fuss he's making is out of all proportion. He's actually manhandling me, screaming "Get out. Get out of my house."

To be honest, I'm not that bothered. I think it's a bit of a laugh. I think her dad is surprised, like Allie when someone whacked him, and a bit shocked to find us there and is simply overreacting on the spur of the moment. Give it time and he'll get over it and laugh about it.

The night's frosty and I'm used to walking. The others are shuffling around, trying to reach decisions about what to do. I'll leave them to it. I guess I can talk Mr Gallagher around because we've done no damage as far as I know. The house is dark but I think the net curtain's moving and he's peeping out of the window like some nosey old woman. Creep.

I'm feeling shivery cold after being thrown out of the warm house. I'm not dressed for a hike so thank god it's not windy and I soon warm up when I get a move on, to enjoy the fifteen mile walk and jog home savouring the crisp morning as my soft boots crunch on the frosty grass and the sun gradually glows, first under cobalt and then clear powder blue. I feel great. My mind's full of thoughts of Diane and me playing things straight and coming out of the evening without trouble, apart from the silly business with her dad. I wonder if he was peeping out of the window. He's either a donkey or an old tart if he was. I go to bed at seven in the morning with dad calling me a dirty stop-out. I'm knackered but happy and glad that neither me, nor Diane were hopped-up on pills.

***

I'm awake. It's three in the afternoon Sunday. I still feel pretty wrecked, not as bad as if I'd been on pills though. I surface slowly and mooch to the kitchen. Mum and Dad are washing up. They're put out because of my sleeping through the day and them having to eat lunch from a coffee table in the back room. Dad asks. "Good night was it? Where were you? Out with this new girl, Diane, was it? You'll not be popular keeping her out those sort of hours. How old is she? If I was her old man I'd be after your guts." He's not joking.

"It was just a daft night. We went to a dance at Dalston. There was a really good group on at a hall over a Smart Western shop but it was packed out so you couldn't move and it looked as though things might turn nasty. We got out and went and had a drink then went back to her place at Brentwood. Things went on a bit and her parents came home and threw us out. It was only one o' clock but the last bus was long gone so I had to walk home. It was a long way, but I quite enjoyed it."

"So you had a bit of a party at her place? What was the party like? Did you make much mess?"

"D'you want me to get the desk-lamp so you can give me a proper third degree." I'm only half laughing. "I only came out here to make a cup of tea. I'm still a bit knackered."

"All your Dad's getting at is, you want to be a bit careful. If you really like this girl how d'you think her parents are going to feel if you keep her out all hours and then finish up making a mess of their house?" Mum knows Diane's the first girl I've been really keen on and she's keen to have me keen. She thinks there's a sort of rightness about it.

"I couldn't help it, it was just the way things turned out and it wasn't a party. There were only five of us and Diane and we hadn't made a mess. If it had been you, you'd probably have put us up on the floor instead of just chucking us out in the freezing cold, in middle of the night. Her old man went barmy for no reason. I'll ring up in a bit and sort it out. He'll be okay, even if he's a bit of a berk. I'll sort him out. Even if I take a bit of stick to take some flack off Diane."

"Well if you like her you'd better be a bit more careful in future." Mum's oiling wheels and smoothing paths as usual.

"Yeah, Yeah ,Yeah. I'll do what I can, but Diane's got a mind of her own and if she wants to do something she'll do it and there's nothing I can do about that. I couldn't put her in a cage if I wanted to. That's one of the things I like about her. She's got a brain and she's fun to talk to. She's not like the girls round here, with her head full of marriage and confetti and rings and babies all the time. She wants to do things. Getting married is one thing and it's okay but there's more to life than getting married; getting lumbered with kids you can't afford; and skewered to a rotten job like mine."

That's shut them up. We don't talk too much about my crap job, that they think could be worse, for their son who could be a bit brighter or at least a bit more steady. Twice I try to phone Diane but twice the phone just cuts off. Pound to a pinch of spit it's her old man

227

acting the 'big I am' again. I suppose I'll have to wait till she calls me.

"I'm going for a walk."

"Well you needn't come back here like a bear with a sore head."

That's Mum. Peace at all costs. She doesn't know what to do either. I felt okay when I went bed. Walking past the church, it crosses my mind I could go and have a swear at the vicar. Silly old twat had no idea what was going on in the real world when I was singing in the choir for half a crown a wedding. Thought I was a little angel. At least he didn't try his luck with a bottle of cider and a hand on my knee the way the Boys Brigade bloke did, so p'raps I'll let the silly old bugger off. I laugh at myself and the vicar and the world. Maybe I should show Diane I'm really interested, and go and threaten to stick one on her old man if he doesn't stop acting like a big kid, hogging all the little ones' lollies. I'd probably be in trouble if I did, and she'd not thank me for it. That stupid song again.

'Though it's dark I see you smile, Diane.' Wish you were here.

***

Monday I'm glad to ride my bike to work. I can burn energy this way, and laugh at daft old buggers sitting in a half stupor, waiting for the traffic lights while I fly past with the blood flowing right to my finger tips, which are warm enough in lambs-wool mittens.

Waiting to see Diane again is pleasurable agony and anything to shorten the wait is good. I've not even heard from her since her dad threw us out and I want to know what's going on. I'm tempted to go and see her, even though it's midweek and will take a whole evening and might cause trouble. I've always been impatient. I like things resolved. That's one thing I'm good at, making decisions. The only difficulty is that to resolve situations, I tend to make the decisions which don't lend themselves to easy resolutions, so I make things worse instead of better. I don't want to make trouble for Diane. It seems she's got trouble enough without me sticking my oar in. The

228

day's scuffing its feet like a ten year old not too keen on getting to school. It'd be really handy if I could clip its ear and tell it to get a move on. There's little to do now the Sultzer Plant job's finished and Gallatia seems to have lost interest in me at the moment.

She doesn't ring till Tuesday and then it's in the morning, so it's Mum who takes the call. "Our Dave's not in the good books with your dad?" I said to her. "I don't blame him. Dave can be silly at times," she said. "It wasn't your fault and her dad's making a lot of fuss. But anyway she'll meet you on Thursday at Harrison Gibson's again at six. She said she might not phone again because her dad's making a fuss, but she'll be there at six. She likes you and you want to be careful. She seems like a nice girl and if you want to get on with her, you'll need to sort things out with her dad and stop playing the anchor's weighed at weekends. Getting in here at six and seven o clock in the morning after going out on Friday night's no way to carry on. We were all young once and I don't begrudge you enjoying yourselves but there's enjoying yourselves and acting daft. You want to pull yourself together and start acting a bit more sensible if you're not going to get her father's back up."

Mum's having a serious go, so she's more than a bit fed up with me. "I didn't intend to be out late and she was home before her parents. If they're that worried you'd have thought they'd have waited up for her, but he was off selling insurance or something and didn't get back till after us, so what's he got to complain about. Anyway I'll see her on Thursday and we'll see what's going on then."

"Well you'd better be in at a reasonable time or you'll be losing the job next, and what will you do then, when you can't put something towards your keep?"

"I won't be late. I'm hardly ever late for work and I don't take time off like some, and this weekend I'm probably working, so you can have some extra if you want." She's a bit sorry she's just said what she did so I'm off the hook, and we leave it at that.

67

Tenter-hooks

I'm treading hot coals waiting for Thursday. I've fixed up with Bernie and Stan for the weekend. I'd rather spend it with Diane and I need to tell her about what's going on at work, so she doesn't think her dad's going to stop me from seeing her, or that he's frightened me off. I'll tell her that I'm going to go and see him and sort things out and let him know that the last thing I want to do is mess Diane about. I'll tell him it was just a set of mad circumstances that made things pan out as they did. I'll convince him one way or another. Even if he's a creep, he is her dad so he can't be all that bad, not with a daughter like Diane.

***

Thursday 6th October 1966 5.56p.m

I'm at Harrison Gibson's again. I'm early again but nervous in a different way now. I'm sure Diane will come but waiting's a penance. Everything's a mess; the business with her Dad's annoying me because he won't even talk, and that's not fair. The business at work that I'm determined to sort out has come at the most awkward time. I've got to work at the weekend if I'm to find out whether Gallatia's been fiddling, but it may look to Diane and even more so to her dad that I'm avoiding a confrontation with him. The one thing that I don't want is to appear gutless - scared of her dad, mostly because of pride, I suppose, but also because I don't want to start on the wrong foot with him or Diane. I want everything up front and above board, because that's the way I operate. I'll not have anyone thinking they can manipulate me with threats or anything else. I've been brought up to be honest and face trouble head on. There'll be no messing about. I want Diane and I'll put up a fight for her. Anyone who thinks otherwise can think again.

She's here, dead on time, with a crooked smile that could mean anything. "You look like thunder," she laughs. I kiss her cheek and squeeze her hand.

"Everything seems messed up at the moment. At work things are going on that I want to sort out, and there's this daft rubbish with your Dad, and not even being able to talk to you during the week is bugging me. Give us a kiss an' I'll buy you a cake."

"Can I have a coffee as well?"

"That'll be an extra kiss."

"Cakes and coffee for kisses, what-ever next? I hope you're not trying to buy me off. I don't come cheap, you know," as she grabs my hand, giving me a flirty look and gently biting my thumb.

"Stop it. you'll get me flustered."

"That's a new name for it." She's pulls me towards the counter with one hand and picks up a self serving tray with the other."

"D'you treat all the blokes like this?"

"You make me want to. I want you to kiss me, and I want you to buy me cake, and no I've never felt like this before. You make me like it."

The woman behind the counter's standing, hand on hip, looking at us saying nothing but making clear she wants us to make up our minds and stop messing about. She's staring at us impatiently. We glance at one another, disregarding her, but then I say "Two coffees please," and, looking at Diane, "What cake can I buy you off with?"

"I'm choosey, you know, but coffee with chocolate cream will probably do it," as she leans towards me, pulling a face and poking out the tip of her tongue and wriggling it.

"You're flustering me again. Stop it."

She's giggling as I pay. We sit down and tidy the table and I put the tray on an empty table nearby. Turning back to her, I say "Hello, I'm glad you're here." She says "Hello, it's a pleasure." We hold hands. It's pathetic but gives me a lump in my throat. I draw my hand away and take a mouthful of coffee. Her eyes are damp.

"My Dad's being rotten. I could only come tonight because it's his insurance association night. He doesn't want me to see you. He says if you were any good you wouldn't be taking me to dives in London where they're playing black music. He says it's degenerate and you're a yob and he's not having me acting like a tart."

"It's a good job I wasn't there. Did you tell him you met me there, and you'd gone with Louise and I didn't take you?"

"I couldn't tell him that, he'd go mad. I don't know what he'd do. I told him you're not a yob and I want to see you."

"What does your Mum say?"

"She's all right. She'd leave it up to me but she's scared of Dad and never says anything."

I tell her "I don't know what we should do, but I've got to work on Saturday." I go into details about the suggestion and keeping the records and that I think that people are fiddling; and that if I can prove it, it'll change things a lot, so Saturday is out for me anyway.

"I can meet you tomorrow night though, if you want, and in the evening on Saturday."

"Dad won't let me out tomorrow. He's treating me as though I'm fourteen and he's saying he's not going to let me out on Saturday morning because he needs me in the shop and it's not fair to Mum if I'm not there. If I go out on Saturday night he wants me in by half past ten." Then thoughtfully, "What I could do though, if you want, is tell Mum I want to invite you round to tea on Saturday, so that they can meet you properly. It's a bit old fashioned but I don't think he'll moan too much if we do it like that."

"I'll do whatever you think's best, but I'll have to watch my temper. I want to hit him already."

"You do anything like that and I'll kill you. You might not like him, but causing trouble like that would only make things worse. You'll be on your best behaviour, then it'll make it hard for him to be rotten."

"Will he let you ring me if you do that. I'd like it best if we could just ring one another like normal people. I've been dying to talk to you all week. Couldn't you at least get him to let you ring me

232

whenever you want. Have you told him you don't want to be a nun? Tell him I think it'd be a waste for you to be a nun." She squeezes my hand and says "Eat your cake. I'm not going to be a nun. And I'll get him to let me phone, but be careful, he may want to listen."

"God, I thought my Dad could be a pain, but both my parents are saints next to your dad. How d'you put up with him?"

"I didn't choose him. He's being a pig at the moment, but sometimes he can be really nice."

I keep my mouth shut. I still want to hit him. We finish our coffee and then walk, enjoying each other's company till it's kissing time and early buses. We're both tempted to stay late but know the world won't go away, however much we wish it. We both have to work tomorrow.

68

Fiddles For Sure

Friday 7th October 1966 7.57a.m

I clock in but don't do anything worth talking about. The sinter plant job's finished and Small's doing any real drawing office work. It's clear Gallatia's got me in the office because he wants to know where I am. I've given up bothering about him and have spent time wandering around the plant, chatting to people I get on with. Quite funny when I think about it; perhaps I should start a blast furnace social club. I've only got four months to go now till the apprenticeship's over and I'm thinking Gallatia can go boil his head or do something even more ludicrous and much more rude. Something's bound to happen. I'll bet I'm driving him crazy. He hasn't sacked me yet and I'm pretty sure I know why. All being well I'll find out tomorrow.

***

Saturday morning - I'm in early and straight into my overalls and down to the By-products. Stan's there already, sitting smoking on a fork truck outside the gate.

"Morning kid. How ya' doing? Good day for a bit of fun. Have you been into the office yet?"

"Morning Stan. Can't get in. The door's locked, but I can get through the window okay. Wait till Bernie's in and we'll get the pump out.   Then I'll go into the office if you two're okay stripping the pump."

"Right, we might as well get started.   Bernie's probably playing with the baby." (His wife had a baby a few weeks ago and Bernie's full of it. We wonder if he thought he might not be able to because of his war wounds. We've been pulling his leg rotten because he's made such a fuss about it. We're pleased for him really.)

I get the tools while Stan rigs rope around the pipe, ready to pull the pump out of the water. We'll lift it out with one of the forks. We're not supposed to do it like that. It's dangerous but we don't have a mobile crane, so it's the only way we can do the job unless we rig some sort of gantry, and that would mean a lot of work. We've done it this way before, and as long as we're careful we're confident it'll be okay.   No-one's asked how we're going to do it, and Rance will assume this is how it'll be done. No one bothers much about safety till there's an accident. We're just about ready when Bernie arrives.

"Morning - looks as though you don't need me. P'raps I'll piss off home again; she had a proper go at me this morning for working overtime on Saturday. I'm supposed to spend it today, not earn it." He's showing off but we know he's crazy about his Missis and the baby, so he's seriously putting himself out, coming in today. We take no notice and between the three of us have soon got the pump out of its filthy muddy tank. Bernies's got one of the labourers in to drain the tank and shovel muck out. By the state of it, it looks as though it needed doing. It's nearly lunchtime and while no one's around we ride

234

up to the main workshop on the fork truck and take over the canteen to eat our lunch, then it's into the office.

I'm nervous. I'll be breaking in. It's not as if there's anything of value in there, but I need to get into Gerrard's filing cabinets. We size up the job of getting me through the window. Stan's having fun driving the truck over the rough ground at the back of the office, playing stock cars. He's like a big kid. He's dafter than me and he's nearly fifty. He has me stand on the forks and lifts me so that all I have to do is squeeze through the window. Once I'm in it'll be quite difficult to get out and I'm trembling half with fear and half exhilaration.

Inside and I thought the filing cabinets might be locked, but they're not. It takes a while for me to work out how the system works, but it's simple enough. I settle down after a while, even though it's eerily quiet. It's going to take a while and I find that it's almost impossible to go through the files without taking them completely out of the cabinets. I think that's best because I can hide myself from the line of vision through the glass door. I do need to be careful, though, that I get the files back in the right places, otherwise Gerrard might smell a rat. I need to check nearly a year's requisitions, and there are a lot. To do the job thoroughly would take days, so I'll have to whiz through and hope I don't miss too much. I soon realise there are numbers missing with no explanation why. That in itself is incriminating but doesn't help me prove that they've been getting bearings we don't need. The crafty bastards have weeded out the sheets that incriminate. It shows that something's not right, but doesn't give clear proof of what's going on.

After two hours I check to make sure everything's tidy and wriggle back out of the window. I've written down the numbers I know are missing. It looks as though there are more missing than would be accounted for in bearings. Someone's ripping off the Company and they're not doing it by halves. I wonder how they're doing it. Are they selling the stuff or have they got contacts at the suppliers who are paying them. I walk down to the By-products with

235

my list of missing requisitions. Bernie's in the workshop with Stan while the pump's in pieces and they're mostly clean, so the job's probably going well.

"You escaped with your life then," says Bernie with a laugh,

"There are one or two in but no one's been into the offices, have they?"

"If they have I've not seen or heard 'em'."

"Did you find anything out?"

"Not as good as I hoped. They're one step ahead - almost. There are a load of requisition numbers missing and I couldn't find any for sinter plant wheel bearings. Here is a list of the numbers that I had time to make sure are missing."

"Bloody hell - fucking thieving bastards are milking it for all they're worth. That Gerrard's a dark horse all right. Who'd have thought he'd be into that kind of thievery. I wonder if Gallatia's twisting his arm with something really big. Gallatia's got to be in on it. The longer you're around this fucking place, the more it looks like a home for the fuckin' lost and lonely from Wormwood Scrubbs." Stanley's getting poetic.

69

A Tea Party at Diane's

Saturday October 8th 1966 6.10 p.m

I didn't have to come on a bus tonight. Stan gave me a lift on his way home, so I'm early. I had a shower in the new locker room. It's the first time I've used it and I'm feeling pleased with myself on that score. It's basic and functional but I'd rather be there than in the hot seat bog. It might only be functional, but it's a good job, not shoddy, flashy and tin-pot.

I'm in two minds. I'm itching to squeeze Diane, but at the same time I'm half ready to blow raspberries at her dad for starters. I'm a bit nervous. They've got a bellpush with a little light in and a printed label that says Lockwood. There were lots of them on the paper round - Took me weeks to realise Lockwood was the makers name. I kept thinking I was at the wrong house. I feel a bit like that now.

At home we've got a knocker that's polished till it gleams. Theirs is not even a bell. I'm wondering if it's got a regular repertoire or just plays the one thin tubular bell tune when Diane opens the door. She puts out a hand to pull me in but I pull her out while the door's not open very wide and give her a big hug and kiss, but after first melting she wriggles free, pushing me away, whispering "Leggo" which I do and she does the female straightening her clothes thing, patting herself down, keeping me in order, saying "Ssh... Stop it - best behaviour," trying to look severe school marm but with a hint of a smile as we go in. I hate that. We can't even say hello properly. Her bloody Old Man's always in the way.

I'm not aware of the house from the other night. There was too much going on. It's bigger than I thought, bigger than ours by miles, a pre-war three-bed semi, but a good size. The hallway is well decorated with stylish wallpaper, art-decoish, a bit dated, predominantly light grey with geometric shapes and thin lines of primary reds and yellows. The doors I can imagine made with four panels, one square at the top and three long narrow ones below, but they've been covered with hardboard trimmed around the edge with quarter round beading pinned on, and all painted white. It's a shame, it would look much better without the hardboard. The banister's had the same treatment. It's boxed in. It's neatly done but although painted white, it makes the place claustrophobic. It makes me think of crownwheels. The banister should be left open at least. The whole is carpeted thick plain grey. It smells unfamiliar but fresh, and the carpet's nice and warm feeling.

Her dad appears, framed in the doorway of the sitting room. She's right about him. He's slim and taller than me. There's a sharpness about his features and he has a pencil moustache and slicked back dark hair. He looks arrogant and vain. Men with moustaches often worry me. Too frequently they're vain, fiddling about, neither shaving nor bearded. He's wearing a brownish mixed check two-piece suit and fussily patterned brown brogues on a Saturday night at home.

On a hook on the wall is a tan gabardine raincoat and brown trilby. He really looks the part of a Raymond Chandler 'operator,' every inch a bloody insurance salesman. I'm flummoxed by him, thinking he might slip into a spiel and offer me an insurance policy, like a Jehovah's witness on a loop you can't switch off. His moustache is wider but less deep than Hitler's, but still makes me think he's obsessive, otherwise he'd not be bothered with such fiddly nonsense. The other night we hadn't had much on in the way of lights, and everything happened fast. Diane's right, he's so different from her, I don't like him from the moment I see him.

The instant animosity is mutual. We can't help feeling the way we do about people. I can't like him any more than I could dislike his daughter. He's driving his lovely daughter away, stupid, creepy man. The family name isn't Lockwood like in the bellpush. It's Galloway.

Mrs Galloway's thin, in truth a bit scrawny. She reminds me of the coxcomb on a chicken's head and under its chin. I'd want to laugh if it wasn't that she doesn't look well. Although her skin is red, she looks washed out, her fairish greying hair looking thin and lacklustre. The clothes she wears attempt to be bright but her droop shouldered harassed look manages to make them dowdy.

Diane holds my hand while looking carefully towards her father, saying, "Dad, this is Dave." I move towards him and he takes a step forward, moving rudely in front of Diane. She lets go my hand as I raise it towards him to shake, being very formal, saying, "I'm sorry about the other night but we weren't really doing any harm Mr Galloway."

He reluctantly returns my grip with a limp, swift, cursory

shake, withdraws his hand, folds his arms stiffly, puffing out his chest, confrontational, challenging, and says, "You took Diane to that seedy club in the West End where they play the black music?"

I'm nonplussed, nervous with my head full of images of Diane in the joyful days recently gone. There's a pause as I gather my thoughts and answer, "Yes."

"Would you take her there again?"

"Well, yes, if she wanted to."

"And what would you say if I said I didn't want you to?"

I think, bloody hell he's worse than Gallatia. Diane and I move instinctively closer. Our hands meet anxiously, gripping tight, supporting each other. Mrs Galloway has moved behind her husband and looks flustered, but says nothing. There's another long pause. We're all embarrassingly close together in the small space of the hall, whilst I take time to think. Galloway (I've already started to think of him as Galloway) tries to look the outraged Victorian patriarch, but that silly pencil moustache lets him down. I could either laugh in his face or flatten his pointy nose but say,

"Is this fair? We've only known one another a few weeks, and I think Diane is the nicest girl I've met. What happened last weekend might have been a bit daft but we weren't doing anything wrong." It was absolutely the right thing to say because I really meant it. It stopped him in his tracks and quite surprised me. In a thin twittery voice from behind Galloway, Mrs Galloway says, "Tea's nearly ready, Frank. It's your favourite: salmon and tomato sandwiches and I've got Scotch eggs and a good pork pie with some lettuce and tomatoes, then there's jelly and tinned fruit salad and cream."

I still can't believe she's their daughter. Mum would have just served it up and expected people to enjoy it. A good job I'm wearing a nondescript Harris Tweed sports jacket and not the Paisley one. He'd have gone berserk. Could they really be her parents? Mine let me make up my own mind and take the consequences, whilst providing some support. Clearly families in Brentwood operate very differently. Diane's tense, gripping my hand tightly. Galloway pushes past us with a sharp,

"I'm going to wash my hands."

Diane quickly squeezes my fingers a couple of times and says,

"We'll lay the table Mum," trying to relieve the tension hanging in the air, more apparent than the smell of tailor made cigarettes."

She pulls me into the front room, where there's a big dining table, pecks me on the cheek, giving a coy grin on her way to a sideboard where she draws out a table cloth and, throwing it open onto the table, says, "Well, help me then." A huskiness in her voice fills me with delicious emotion. I'm her genie. Her voice is a spell. She can talk me into anything at this moment. I'll fight her Dad to the death she only has to say the word. Conspiratorial, enjoying our secret intimacy, we whisper as we lay the table and make trips to the kitchen to get the sandwiches and other bits and pieces. We hear Mrs Galloway's hushed apologetic call, "Its ready Frank."

There's no reply and Galloway honours us with his presence only after we're sitting and pouring tea. Mrs Galloway makes conversation, asking, "What did you do today, Dave?" I'm too busy thinking Galloway's a pig to answer, but Diane says, "He's been working." I say "Yes I had to work today. It wasn't nearly as pleasant as last Saturday when Diane and me wandered around Romford."

"So you didn't just fritter the day away this week then," says Galloway, viciously stabbing a pearl onion then looking at me as if he wished I was on the fork. Mrs Galloway, twittering again, says, "I want to look at curtains. I might have come in the afternoon if I'd known. I do like shopping and I want to look at curtains. Did you go into the new Harrison Gibsons? Is it as good as they say? I really want to see what curtains they've got." Galloway grunts. "Hmm, fritter away money, as well as time. Have you finished last month's books yet?"

Mrs Galloway looks sadly at her sandwich, saying nothing. Seconds drag their feet as we eat in silence. We pass around the jelly, fruit and cream so solemnly, we might be playing Russian roulette.

The silence is tangible and then more tea. That helps a bit - good old tea. Everyone always feels more relaxed when there's tea around.

"So you enjoyed your day wandering around Romford, wasting time with my daughter... Dave? Wasn't it cold? I wouldn't have thought it was a day for sitting in the park?"

"It was the best Saturday I've had in a long time, Mr Galloway and I think Diane enjoyed it too, didn't you Di."
That's the first time I've called her Di'. Somehow it brings us closer."

He doesn't give her a chance to answer.

"You needn't think you're going to do that every Saturday. We have to open the shop in the mornings and I need Diane there as well as her mother. I never know when I'll have to go out and we need two in the office. Damn curtains don't grow on trees" - almost snarling at his wife.

I'm embarrassed. I say nothing. I just want to go. Forget the tea. An image of him as I pour it over his head goes through my mind. Mrs Galloway quietly scurries around, clearing the tea things, nervous, like a mouse in a hurry, trying to keep her feet off the floor to keep down the noise, and Diane gets up to help. I stand to join in. Galloway roughly pushes back his chair, making noise enough for us all, and stands to light a cigarette, saying, with a hint of a smirk at me, "Let them clear away, too many cooks and all that," and goes next door to the sitting room.

Rather than join Galloway, I sit back down. Diane gives me an unhappy look, her soft brown eyes magnified by welling tears, I don't know whether of frustration, sadness or anger. She scrambles out, carrying tea things. I set about moving what's left to one end of the table.

When she comes back, I feel awkward. I want to hug her and be reassuring, but he might come in and cause more unpleasantness. I take her hand and give it a small squeeze, and draw her quite close. She looks at me with an apologetic smile. I touch her face gently with the back of my fingers doing my best to reassure her, my muscles knotted, and breathing fast, watching the vein in her neck pulse, anxious, unhappy. Stretched taut with wanting to hug her, I ask quietly but driven,

"What do you want to do, it's only early?"

"I think you'd better go. I didn't think it would be this bad." The tea hangs in the hollow of my stomach and it's difficult to breathe. Words come automatically.

"Okay, but only if you really think so. I'd rather you came with me." I look at her hard, feeling something's just broken. She's near tears and I'm not so far off. She calls into the front room, "Dave's just going Dad."

He appears again, framed in the doorway, arms folded, face showing that same half smirk. He steps back to let us pass, ushering us out, arms at twenty past eight, as though shooing out a pair of dogs that have walked uninvited through his door. I turn and stop, trying to act normally, calling, "Good night, Mrs Galloway thanks for the tea," and more quietly, "Good night Mr Galloway."

I'm feeling powerless and childish, wanting to scream at him and kick and yell, but impotent because of Diane. I take her hand more roughly than I want because I'm fragmented, head, arms and legs all pulling in different directions, pulling her behind me to the front gate. I could pick her up and run off with her like a thief; I could pick her up and hug her like a doll; or carry on dragging her behind me, really causing a scene; but I do the conventional thing and let her disentangle her fingers and close the gate, shutting me out. She leans forward, offering her cheek for a genteel kiss. I grab her shoulders and kiss her hard, wanting her to come with me, then whisper, huskily, "Call."

She turns away, downcast, under the critical eyes of her father. I walk away in turmoil, looking back to see the door closing, shutting out the light, leaving only darkness. He's already led her indoors. I stand at the bus stop still not whole, the pieces still not together. After such a good day, how quickly things have changed. On the bus, watching people going about on Saturday night, lively, silhouetted against bright-lit shops, smiling and laughing full of anticipation. On Friday I was one of them, looking forward to a tremendous night with

242

good things ahead, but now I'm on the way home, alone, thinking about this girl, the only girl I've ever thought I'd really want to have and hold… It's a long time since I've felt like crying.

ৠৠ৶৶

70

Relief and Disappointment

Thursday October 11th 1966 8.00a.m

Not long to go now and I'll be twenty-one and a City and Guilds qualified fitter. The years of purgatory that are the apprenticeship are nearly over. Soon I can leave Fords and Gallatia, with the piece of paper that has cost me so much. My only thought now is how that will fit in with anything that happens with Diane?

Gallatia's attitude seems to have changed; the looks he gives me convey expectancy, although he still doesn't speak. I'm back in the awful situation of having little real work to do, just fill-in jobs, so that I have to sit in the office and give the impression I'm working. This gives me time to think about Diane, her father and mother, and constantly mull over how Thursday will develop. On Wednesday evening she still hasn't phoned to say the meeting is still on. Thursday comes and the hours pass, a slow stream of something thick and foul, but finally the clock hands, cold and impersonal, reach four o' clock. My hands are hot and sweaty and my fingers bloated. I go straight to Romford. I ring Mum to confirm that Diane has phoned to say she's still coming. My tongue feels swollen and tastes sour.

"Yes she said she was coming but she didn't say anything else. She didn't seem to want to talk. She wasn't chatty at all. She said she'd be at Harrison Gibson at six." I walk, tense, passing the shops

243

unseeing, worrying that my watch is wrong, the minutes pass so slowly. I'm in the coffee shop twenty minutes early and sit trying to read a newspaper, unable to concentrate for more than seconds, my body an irritant to my brain, that wants me near Diane. I want to pace around looking out for her. When she arrives, she looks wan. Whatever she has to say isn't good. The usual animation in her face is missing. Trying to act naturally, I ask, "Coffee? What about a cake?" She gives a sad smile. I pause, hoping for a kiss. "I'd like a coffee and a piece of the coffee gateau." We queue together. I squeeze her hand before she picks up a tray. She won't let me pay. We sit at a table in a corner, where the paper I've been trying to read is spread untidily before my half empty cup. I sweep it away. She carefully sets down her tray and puts the coffee and cake on the table. I pick up the tray as an excuse to touch her hand.

"What happened after I went?"

"Nothing much really; I went and helped Mum with the washing up. She likes you.
Then I went to bed to read." There are tears in her eyes.

"Eat your cake and we'll walk." I pick up the newspaper.

"D'you think we dare look at the horoscopes?"

"Yours first," she says, blinking back the tears.

"Aquarius: look out for opportunities. It may be a good time to travel and make new friends or acquaintances."

"What's mine?"

"What are you?"

"Sagittarius."

"Keep your feet on the ground. This is a time when you need to take care with relationships. Don't get carried away in the heat of the moment. There may be some money coming your way if play your cards right."

"Dad might give me my wages tomorrow," she says, the tears welling in her eyes.

"So horoscopes were tempting fate. Are you sure you want that cake?" She's hardly touched it. I pick up my teaspoon and aim as though to take some.

"Get off." Ah, better, a spark. I smile.

She smiles back. "I hate thieving men."

"You should have let me buy it."

"So you could take it back again. No thanks, I'd rather pay for it myself, then it's mine and thieving men can keep their hands off." She concentrates on eating while I watch, feeling a little happier.

We leave and I guide her towards the park without thinking. I'm not used to being with girls and normally would feel awkward, but with Diane things just happen. We're a fit like a good dovetail joint. We walk a while in silence, both dejected.

"So what really happened when I left?"

"Oh, it was just like I said, nothing. I helped mum with the washing up and then went to bed. It was Sunday morning before anything happened. Mum never argues, but Dad sort of argues with himself and then blames her. That's what he did on Sunday morning." The tears are coming again now. I pull her close with my right arm and she buries her head in my shoulder. Her body shudders as she cries and the words come in a flood. "Then he hit her. He's slapped her before but never really hit her. He punched her and she just flopped down and laid there. I thought he might kick her. I grabbed his shoulder and shouted at him to stop and then he pushed me off, hard against the wall, and it really hurt. He's never treated me like that before. It's as if he hates us. He made us stay in the bedrooms; then he told me to stay where I was and dragged mum downstairs to make the dinner. He dragged her, I could tell, like a bag of washing, and kept shouting at her, telling her she was useless and a nuisance; and he was shouting up the stairs at me, calling me a tart. He called you awful things too. And he raved about Mum spending money on rubbish, screaming on about curtains. It's as though he's going mad and I don't know what to do."

By now, she's hanging onto me, wracked by sobs and I don't know what to do either. People are giving me dirty looks as though I'm making her cry.

"What time have you got to be home? And where is he now?"

"They've gone to an insurance association dinner. That's why I could come tonight; they won't be back till late, about midnight probably. He's put special locks on the doors so we can't get out. He's even put bolt things on the windows that you need a special key for, but Mum's got one of the keys that he doesn't know about, that's how I got out tonight. He's got a lock on the phone as well so we can't phone out. And I don't know what to do."

"We make a fine pair, you and me. I've got to escape from Dagenham and Fords and you've got to escape from your dad. You're worse off than me though. Have you got any money?"

"It's not just that; I've got to think about Mum. If I had loads of money I couldn't just go and leave Mum. He's terrible to her and if I'm there it's not quite so bad for her - and he's getting worse. I don't know what's the matter with him. He's always had a temper, but nothing like now."

She's mentioned a brother. "What about your brother?"

"He's living near Aldgate. He's got a flat. He works at the Stock Exchange; I don't really know what he does. All I know is he makes plenty of money, but he fell out with Mum and Dad years ago. He's eight years older than me. He's been gone for years; I hardly know him really. He got away from Dad after loads of rows. It was awful then. If he did anything now it would probably make things worse."

There's nothing to be done. We walk and settle to simply consoling one another. I tell her about the dinner to celebrate the completion of the Sultzer Plant conversion and that they'd said to bring my girlfriend. That brings the lump to my throat again.

"Celebration - It makes you feel like buying a bloody shotgun."

That's the first time I've sworn while I've been with her. There's nothing to be done. We can't even communicate unless she calls or writes. There's no way I can contact her. I take her home and we kiss gently, forlorn, before I help her climb through the window into their sitting room. I let go her arm, slowly, squeezing softly, I

246

could climb in too but I say, "Write, phone or come to my place anytime." I'm weak and gutless but there's nothing to fight. She gives a small wave. Resigned, I wave back, jaw locked and swallowing. My tongue's not thick now, it's mobile and there's lots of saliva. I can just make out her face at the front window as I leave. It's dark and she hasn't turned the light on.

With the lump in my throat I catch the bus, annoyed with myself for not climbing in with her. He'd have had to really take me on then and he wouldn't have had a good reason for throwing me out. I'm gutless. I should have gone with her but I did what I did and it's done. You only get one chance at some things. The lump's still there. It's late when I get home but Mum has waited up.

"What happened?" she asks.

"Nothing really, her Dad's locking her up like a prisoner and she won't leave because she thinks he'll beat her Mum up. It seems as though he's more or less nuts. There's nothing I can do." I don't like saying it. I feel ashamed.

"D'you want some cocoa.?

"No thanks, I don't feel very good. I'll just go to bed."

71

A Celebration?

Friday October 9th 1966 6.40 a.m

I wake to the thought - And today is a day of celebration - just another of life's little ironies. I dress as usual and ride my bike as usual. All that has changed is that my hopes have been raised and dashed like those of someone dying in the desert, overflowing with newfound optimism at the sight of an oasis, only to have his relief torn away on understanding it's just a mirage. It seems more important than ever now to escape bloody Fords.

I clock in as usual, hang my jacket on the back of my seat as usual, and set about sharpening my pencils. Peering around my drawing board, the spring light makes even the back of the sinter plant chimney fan casing look interesting, rather than downright ugly. I wonder what their celebration will be like. Shame Diane won't be there. That lump's in my throat again. I wonder if something rotten will happen - as usual.

I check with Mrs Short to make sure that everyone knows I'm going to their celebration.

"Oh don't worry about that. They're even sending a car for you, and they said for you to pick up your girlfriend on the way. It sounds as though you should wear a suit. Maybe you should change on the way." I'm being made a fuss of, so she's fluttering today.

I wonder what's going on, they're treating me as though I've won the pools or something. What the hell, I'll be gone in two months. I won't change; there isn't any point. I wouldn't stay, even if they offered me Gallatia's job.

***

The hotel's swanky, everything polished and spotless, and there are big expensive bouquets on either side of the foyer doors. Everything looks new and expensive. A girl sitting beside the desk clerk looks expensive too. She's wearing black - a suit cut to show all the right bumps in all the right places and just enough creamy cleavage to be seductive with the skirt (if you could call it that) cut fashionably short. She ushers me to the room where the event is taking place. It's set out like a wedding. The man I assume to be boss of the contractors sits in the place of the groom with Charles on the right beside him. A woman sits on his left. I'm the only one I recognise as being from Fords and I'm on the top table. The expensive looking girl who brought me in ushers me to my place, gives me a menu, and asks what I'd like to drink.

It begins to look as though this whole jolly is an oblique backhander, and I want to fly a flag to show I'm not in the market. I ask "Do you have any White Shield Bass and, if so, can I have it brought carefully, not shaken, and not cold, with a bottle opener so that I can open it properly." She's cool, and smiling, says, "I'll check, but I think wine might be more appropriate, given the menu."

I don't put my thumb to my nose as I say, "There's plenty of time yet." I guess it's in my mind to have a good drink, even if I don't get legless and make a fool of myself. It strikes me that I might have brought the Paisley jacket. It would raise some eyebrows amongst this crowd. Their suits are strictly East End, all tapered trousers and padded shoulders. The women, apart from Miss Expensive, wear skirts nearly to the knee with big bold prints and big bouffants to match, and make-up that could have been applied by the plasterers working on the job we're celebrating. They look almost pre-war. Give them credit, though, they have the White Shield and they serve it as requested. The boss raises his glass to me and nods. Charles shakes his head in mild disgust.

The menu is quite something: caviar, lobster, oysters, described in French and English. I've not seen anything like it. I get through some caviar for a starter and then go on to whiting with peeled grapes; it's tasty but so is a nice piece of roast lamb with mint sauce. There's fancy wine that comes in grubby bottles with dirty labels that's okay too. It definitely has the edge on EMVA Cream and is a bit more interesting than Harvey's but it's wasted on me. I just want to get comfortably pie-eyed, an objective I achieve a bit earlier than anticipated.

They start with speeches while I'm still working on my sweet. The sweet is fine, but starting the speeches before the meal is finished, is a 'bit off' I think, but if you come down to it, I think the boss is a bit off. He 'sets the ball rolling'. He doesn't swear once but it's obvious he knows how. His jokes aren't risqué, they're plain crude, and Miss Expensive, who seems to have the role of hotel troubleshooter, prances out with a moue. She clearly thinks she's above that sort of thing. Laughable, she knows all the words, I'll guarantee. She's just a silly snob tart with nothing of any consequence in her head. The boss passes the baton to Charles, whose performance is more creditable, with something much closer to real humour.

Then it's my turn. I've not anticipated anything like this. I'm not quite at the slurring stage but already I'm well lubricated enough not to care. I'd clam up if I was sober. I'd enjoy saying 'You can all fuck off with your flashy dinners and your arse licking.' But I'd have to walk out if I did, and I'm not too sure I'd manage it. At the back of my fuddled mind, niggling away, is the fact that I'll be wandering about in the middle of nowhere, three parts pissed, looking for buses. I say to myself 'fuck it' and simply propose a toast.

"To apprentices 'on probation' and jobs well done. Oh and a nice drop of quality plonk and lovely uncomplicated girls without much makeup." At that I sit rather heavily in my chair. Only Charles and perhaps his boss come near understanding, but I get a bit of laughter, not from the 'ladies' though.

After that things degenerate and I get maudlin bored. Even though I'm far from sober, I think they're a cloddish lot. At seven o' clock we wind up and I'm invited to go on to a club. I burble my excuses and they call me a cab and present me with one of the bottles of wine with grubby labels. I cling to it like it's a lifebelt, all the way home. It's something to think about. I'm still the worse for wear when I get home, but I make an effort to stay upright and keep my eyes open while watching the box while Mum watches me. After a couple of hours and a couple of cups of tea the room settles down and loses its tendency to spin. I'm just about fit for bed.

My weekend is flat. I'm hollow and hung over. My mouth tastes of old boxing gloves, but I start scanning the papers for jobs. I can't face the thought of another dead end, mindless engineering job and there are ad's for engineers for the merchant navy. I'm going to run away. I don't seem to have much option. I'm ashamed of that too. I should have made myself options, somehow found a way of facing up to things better. I've just made a pig's ear of everything I've touched. I'll call Diane on Thursday though, when her people might be out. Maybe there's something to salvage. I'm not totally gutless, but 'Ah fuck it.' Anything will be better than staying shackled to Dagenham and Fords or somewhere similar and ashamed and annoyed with myself for not having given my all to getting Diane. But I could still go back and take Galloway on. I'm not scared of him. It's the rumpus that worries me. The rumpus and fuss and upset - I'm not supposed to make a fuss and if I do she might be as annoyed as all the rest. 'Fuck it.'

Monday, I'm sitting at my drawing board feeling vacant. Gallatia catches my eye and signals me to come to his office. An interview means little to me. I don't know if he expects me to be nervous, frightened or argumentative. I'm unconcerned. In my mind I'm already gone.

He asks. "Did you enjoy yourself on Friday?"

"It was interesting and I was pleased that they were happy with the job and the meal was good. I'm sure it cost a lot too, but I'm really used to plain food and I'd just as soon have had roast lamb."

"Determined not to be impressed, hmm. You may not realise the meal you ate cost about half of one of your week's wages and the bottle of wine you took home the same. Did you think of what they were doing as tokens of appreciation or presents?'

"I didn't think about it one way or the other. I didn't ask for any of it."

"But you did them some favours with the job."

"I had Trevor to help but I asked Frank Rance if it was okay and I just thought it would be good for everybody if it was finished on time."

"But you didn't think to make any effort to renegotiate the contract on the basis that they were using our labour?"

"No. The thought never occurred to me."

"Did Mr Charles offer you anything else for helping while you were doing the job?"

"No. He bought me a coffee when we went to see the stair mould

251

at their works and he showed me the article by Carron and said you knew about it."

"Hmm, and what did you think about that?"
"Not much, though I thought it was an oversimplification and made things sound a lot less complicated than they are."

"Has it entered your head that what you did during the job might be seen as attempting to curry favour with the management of the contractors?"

"No."

"Well, you're young, but given your record of indiscipline and even contempt for the management of this company, I think you ought to consider it. In the meantime there is a shortage of skilled men in the press shop. There's no work for you here at the moment, so I'm going to lend you to them for a while. Are you okay with that?"

"That's fine with me."

"Right, Mr Rance will give you the details.

72

A Last Chat with Bernie

"Hello Bern. Looks like I'm off. D'you want the requisition numbers? You might be able to get Gallatia somehow. He's sending me to the press shop."

"Yeh, well I'll take 'em, you never know. Have you got your figures from the sinter plant?"

"Are you around next Sunday? I can get them then if you want."

"Another lesson? Yeh, that'll be okay. When are you off?"

"Straight away. Don't know if I left any evidence and he's got the wind up. Gerrard's his old self. Hasn't said two words since we got in. I suppose I'd better go. Gallatia might have spies watching and I've pushed my luck rotten lately. Haven't done any proper work for nearly a month. Something was bound to happen. Be typical if he suddenly decided to sack me a month before the end of the apprenticeship."

"Yeh, well, see you on Sunday. Maybe we'll have a pint. See ya, kid."

***

So there it was, Gallatia had done his best to set me up. The irony was he thought I would be frightened at being accused of taking bribes, because that was how his mind worked. He was actually frightened of me because he couldn't fathom the idea of anyone valuing their independence and integrity more than cash in their pocket. That made me a threat. He thought he was tough, but had no idea that the sort of toughness he valued so much was his weakness. He couldn't accept the idea of anyone who wouldn't be bought, because he saw bribery in the same light as death and taxes. In truth he had no concept of right and wrong, or justice. For him there was just the law and how to avoid getting caught. Moral blackmail meant nothing; he'd stop at nothing. The means, any means, were legitimate tools if they achieved the ends.

That afternoon as I carried my tools on my way to the press shop I phoned for a job advertised with Pacific Asia Navigation and they offered me an interview on the spot. With a little unaccustomed luck I was on my way to new horizons far away, on a ship, away from Dagenham and Fords. I couldn't dance with Diane, but I wouldn't dance to Fords tune either.

73

New Job, New life, but too Easy?

Taking the tube into the city was a change every bit as good as a rest. To see the same things at different times of day is to look at the world through a series of different windows. For me to follow the district line at ten in the morning was a new experience. The carriage had a used look after the rush hour. It was as messy as I'd seen, with litter on the floor and tattered remains of thumbed tabloids on the seats. I'd seldom travelled that way during the day; if I went at all, it was in the evening, on my way to entertainment in the city. The carriage looked more unkempt than it might because of the unaccustomed harsh daylight. Today I was about to step into a new period of my life. I wasn't excited at the prospect. I'd been planning too long and felt matter of fact about the business. I sat opposite two elderly women setting out shopping, and a heavily pregnant, small, pinched looking girl, trying to look inconspicuous as she heaved her awkward bulging belly, around as if annoyed at carrying a heavy shopping bag that she neither owned nor wanted.

I felt detached from the other passengers as we clattered past the smokey yellow brick terraces, fashionable at the end of the 19th century. Now they looked tired, scruffy and mismatched and the gardens, however well tended, had a forlorn unenchanting appearance because flowerbeds, sheds and greenhouses appeared higgledy-piggledy, as though scattered like rubbish. We passed the giant graffiti sign splashed along a hundred yards of concrete wall, asking 'IS SAITCH A DADDY?' Why? And who cares? I asked myself, as always, before we passed into the darkness of the 'tube' proper. Passengers surged and eddied in and out of the carriage, like waves on a beach, as we stopped at the stations, blank faces closed to one another, not communicating, determined to keep a psychological distance from their neighbours, even if they couldn't maintain a physical one. What is it that makes a touch an intrusion or an embarrassment when the right touch from the right person at the right time can be such a joy? Is it the lack of freedom of choice? Is that what made my time at Fords so difficult? Are these regular tube travellers facing and coping with the same problems I had at Fords shutting them out, treating them as though they don't exist? Do they feel enslaved, forced into situations that are only comfortable when entered into with the familiar, the communicative, the known, the loved?

Stepping onto the platform at Aldgate East brought anticipation, nervousness, even excitement. This is where my new life might truly begin. My eyes were dilated after watching dirty looped cables showing black in the weak yellow light from the carriage, hypnotically rising and falling as we rattled along the tunnel under London's streets. Climbing the steps from the dull-lit tube, squinting into bright sunlight above the city's great imposing buildings, I felt insignificant. I lived just ten miles away but it might have been a hundred. I'd never trod this street before. I'd been to the Tower quite a few times; that's where I'd first seen old guns. They were works of art and the lock mechanisms fascinated me. That's the sort of work I'd wanted to do when I left school. I wanted to deal with tricky mechanisms like locks and clocks, hand made with care and pride. I even liked simply looking at them. I'd been to Oxford Street and the museums. I'd walked along Whitehall and the Embankment, but never had I been so conscious of the authority and sheer power that it all represented. I was walking along Leadenhall Street, home to some of the greatest shipping companies in the world.

Finding the right number in elegant foot high bronze figures blackish green with verdigris, solidly attached to the great stone blocks of a building as imposing as any I'd ever entered, I was overawed. I climbed half a dozen big stone steps, ten feet wide, to stand before a pair of polished mahogany doors, big enough to let a lorry through. Turning the great polished brass knob and leaning against the weight of the massive door, I entered a room that matched the scale of the doors. It was huge, cathedral like, but square, making it feel even bigger.

The floor near the entrance was marble. A slightly unkempt man with a grubby frayed white collar was sitting at an untidy tatty, desk, dwarfed by the scale of the room. I walked diffidently towards him. "Ah s'pose you're one o' the blokes answering the ad's abaht jobs are yer'? What's yer name?" Completely wrong-footed by the bald, unmannerly introduction in such apparently hallowed surroundings, I answered "David Ray'. He rudely ignored me saying nothing in reply but picked up one of two phones on the desk. "Got a Mr Ray 'ere abaht a job. Shall I send 'im in?" He put the phone down. "Go to that office over in the far corner." He's pointing, "Watson's on the door. Knock and wait - okay."

I wove between more tatty desks, uncomfortable in unfamiliar territory, through a loud murmur of voices mingling in a ghostly way in the great space above the desk phones. The floor I felt under my feet was more marble, but desecrated by cheap carpet that was hard on the feet like the marble beneath, mocking the grandeur that once proclaimed this building as a shrine to success and commerce. I knocked at the door of a small enclosed prefab' office. "Come in." Entering, I stood before a desk a little better in quality and tidier than those outside. A pasty, thin, undistinguished man half rose and offered a dry white hand to shake. The handshake was reasonably firm. He sat, indicating for me to do the same, saying "Sit down Mr Ray. We won't mess about with a lot of formalities. Have you brought your qualification papers?" I handed him a folder containing the documents. "City and Guilds Mechanical Engineering parts one and two, hmm, distinction, good, that'll do. What about apprenticeship papers?"

"I don't finish until the end of next month."

"Oh, right. Keen to see the sea are you?"

"I'm ready for a move and going to sea should be good experience," I said.

"Well, your qualifications will get you on the ladder, but

they're just the first step. You'll need to study if you're going to get anywhere. How's your maths?"

"It's not my best subject but I've got better since leaving school."

"What sort of money have you been getting?"

"Twenty five pounds a week, without overtime."

"Well you must understand that there is no overtime while you're at sea. You're on call twenty-four hours a day, and we mean twenty-four hours a day. If a ship's engine stops, your job will be to get it started again, and your life can depend on your succeeding. There's no messing about when you're at sea, discipline will be enforced. It's necessary, you can understand that? The money is the same but you get three months leave a year, so the money's good. Does that sound okay?"

"Yes that sounds okay."

"Right. When can you start?"

"Well, Monday after next."

"Right. Can you get in for a medical next week?"

"Yes."

"Right. I'll sort you out with an appointment for our doctor next week and if you pass that okay we'll start you the week after. Is that okay?"

"Yes."

"We'll be in contact, then."

74

Too, Too, Easy?

So Mr Watson was okay even okay, okay, okay. The interview was over. I'd got the job but it was easy and I wondered if it wasn't too easy. It couldn't be worse than Fords, so I hoped it would be... okay.

I could have wandered around the city, taking in the sights, unaccustomed on an ordinary workday, but already I felt a little unnerved, having taken the first step towards my independent adult life. I would not only be leaving home; I would be leaving the country and everything familiar, off to different countries with people I didn't know. I returned to Fords and clocked on for the afternoon. At least I'd earn half a day's money.

I was working in the press shop, among enormous machines where body panels of cars were formed, under tremendous pressure, from flat sheets of steel. The task I'd been given was to carefully remove from a body die some sections that were designed to create drains in the sills of finished cars. Removing these drains would cause the cars to rust more quickly, speeding the time when they would be scrapped. I was there to make cars rot more quickly, so that I could go to work to build more cars more frequently. I couldn't help thinking about the world, and what it was that made it a place where I was forced to do ridiculous things, and accept without question that my elders and betters were wiser and cleverer than me, when the things they forced me to do were clearly wrong.

I had no good reason for criticising capitalism as such. The basic principles seemed perfectly reasonable. It was when things happened that contravened the basic principles that I had trouble. I'd concluded there's nothing wrong with capitalism. The problem as I saw it was corruption. Somewhere in the system there had to be corruption for a situation to exist where the quality of the product was compromised at the behest of management. Adam Smith would have turned in his grave to have such madness attributed to him. If I went on a ship, then we would have a simple job to do, just to get the ship from one place to the next and I would see other parts of the world in the process, which was something that attracted me.

I'd thought about what it is that makes corruption. Commission is okay but corruption is something different. What is that difference? It's surprisingly easy to define. It comes about when people collude to break ethical rules, and for some reason these rules are clear to the great proportion of people in the great proportion of societies. When we're children we call it cheating. Corruption takes place when rules that we all agree to accept to make life bearable are broken, and the perpetrators set out to hide their actions under a veil of secrecy and deception. It takes place when thieves hide their crime behind some kind of screen, and always there is more than one person involved. That's where it differs from fraud; it depends on secret agreements between people. The bigger the organisation, the greater is the opportunity for corruption. Fords was enormous. There were lots of opportunities for corruption, and there were plenty willing to take them.

***

I phoned Diane a few times on Thursdays, but the result was always the same. I still thought of going there and having a go at her Old Man, but I knew I wouldn't do it.

The following Sunday Bernie came for the driving lesson and the first thing he told me was that Gerrard had committed suicide. I couldn't help feeling that the people who, however indirectly, killed Fred and now Gerrard were out there after me, but deep down I knew the problem was Fords. The place was organised so that bastards were always the ones with the upper hand. Someone said scum floats to the top. If the Merchant Navy was crap, it'd be nothing more than Fords all over again, and at least I'd get to travel instead of being stuck like a broken down car in Dagenham.

On Monday the letter arrived for the appointment with the doctor. The date was for the coming Wednesday; they were keen. The doctor's was in a street near East India Dock Road, some distance from Leadenhall Street, but I got there in good time and didn't have to wait long. A nurse ushered me into the surgery. It was a room bigger than might be expected for a surgery and well furnished, in a slightly

259

old fashioned but homely way, with lots of rich coloured hardwood. In the centre of the room was a smart chromium plated medical couch that reminded me of the one we'd purloined for our office in the sinter plant. I laughed at myself reminiscing at twenty-one. I didn't take a great deal of notice of the doctor. I wanted it over and done with.

"Take off your shirt please." I did as instructed; he sounded my chest with his stethoscope. "Take off your shoes and stand under the arm there please." He pointed to a measure on the wall. "Right, stand up straight please." He slid the arm down onto my head. "Step onto the scales please." He looked at the reading. "Right, stand in front of the line and drop your pants please." I did as I was told. "Look right." I looked right. "Cough." I coughed. "Again." I coughed again. "Look left." I looked left. "Cough." I coughed. "Again." I coughed again. "Right, put your pants back on and lie face down on the couch." I did as I was told. He put his stethoscope on my back. "Breath in." I breathed in. He moved the stethoscope. "Again." I breathed in again. "Right, I'm going to measure your legs." I thought, hmm, bit odd. He measured first one and then the other leg. "Your left leg is half an inch shorter than your right and your pelvis slopes to one side. In consequence your spine is slightly bent." He placed his hand on my left buttock. "This side is slightly lower." He squeezed gently. This didn't seem quite right. He placed his other hand on my right buttock and squeezed gently, saying, "And this one is slightly up."

I jumped up. He stepped back, saying "You're not surprised are you? What do you want to go to sea for, with all those men, if you don't want to meet people like me?" I was blushing and not just on my face. I dressed fast. "Oh well, I suppose you've passed," he said, signing a note and handing it to me. "Take that back to Leadenhall Street." I was out of there like a cork from a Champagne bottle. Some introduction to the ways of the Merchant Navy! I was thoroughly unsettled and uncomfortable. 'Hello sailor' isn't just a joke. I was confused and shocked, this didn't augur well for my new career, but what the hell it couldn't be worse than Fords.